Reading Comprehension
IN VARIED SUBJECT MATTER
by JANE ERVIN

9
BOOK

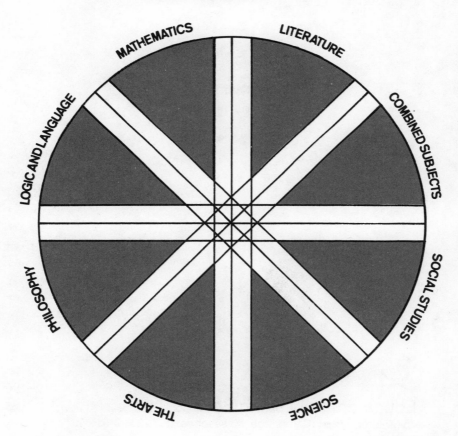

MATHEMATICS · LITERATURE · COMBINED SUBJECTS · SOCIAL STUDIES · SCIENCE · THE ARTS · PHILOSOPHY · LOGIC AND LANGUAGE

Educators Publishing Service, Inc.
Cambridge and Toronto

ACKNOWLEDGMENT

Dr. Ervin would particularly like to thank the editors of the *School Bulletin* of the National Geographic Society for their interest in the development of these books. The inclusion of the *School Bulletin* articles in both adapted and reprinted form has contributed greatly to the quality of this series.

Revised edition, 1981
Fifth printing, 1982

Educators Publishing Service, Inc.
75 Moulton Street, Cambridge, Massachusetts 02238-9101

CONTENTS

subject: combined subjects

Selection 1 — (Sample) Theme: The World of Then and Now
CITIES OF THE FUTURE 1

Selection 2 — Theme: Communication
COMMUNICATING WITH OUTER SPACE 5

Selection 3 — Theme: Transportation
SOME NEW WAYS TO MOVE 9

subject: social studies

Selection 4 — Theme: What America Means—Traditions and Symbols
MOTHER'S DAY 13

Selection 5 — Theme: The Story of America
THE ALOHA STATE 16

Selection 6 — Theme: Great Americans
CIVIL RIGHTS 20

Selection 7 — Theme: How Others Live
A TRIP TO MOSCOW 24

Selection 8 — Theme: Human Relations
THE AMBIGUOUS ATOM 28

Selection 9 — Theme: Human Feats
DIANA NYAD 31

Selection 10 — Theme: Stories with Something to Say
FOR THE GOOD OF HUMANITY 34

subject: science

Selection 11 — Theme: The "How To" Series
HOW TO OUTWIT YOUR OPPONENT 38

Selection 12 — Theme: What is the Biggest?
STARS 41

Selection 13 — Theme: Getting to Know Yourself
THE DIVING WOMEN OF KOREA AND JAPAN 45

Selection 14 — Theme: The World Around Us
DIAMONDS 49

Selection 15 — Theme: The World of Animals, Insects, and Reptiles
BORROWING FROM NATURE 52

Selection 16 — Theme: World of Water, Sea, and Fish
LAND RECLAMATION 55

Selection 17 — Theme: World in the Sky
HEAT FROM THE SUN 58

subject: philosophy, logic, and language

Selection 18 — Theme: What Do You Think?
A DREAM 61

Selection 19 — Theme: The Why and How of It
HOW BIG IS THE UNIVERSE 64

Selection 20 — Theme: Thinking about Life and Its Meaning
WAR 67

Selection 21 — Theme: Words, Words, Words
WHERE DO THEY COME FROM? 70

subject: mathematics

Selection 22 — Theme: How about That?
RUBBER SHEET GEOMETRY 73

Selection 23 — Theme: Figuring the Facts
THE TOPSY-TURVY WORLD OF TOPOLOGY 76

Selection 24 — Theme: Seeing the Facts
A TWISTED WORLD OF ONE-SIDED FIGURES 80

subject: literature

Selection 25 — Theme: Myth, Folklore, and Fantasy
THE END OF THE WORLD 83

Selection 26 — Theme: Rhythm, Repetition, and Sound
TWO POEMS 86

Selection 27 — Theme: How Others Have Said It
WORKING FOR CHANGE 89

Selection 28 — Theme: How Others Have Described It—Houses and Homes
OCEAN VIEW 92

Selection 29 — Theme: Different Literary Forms and Styles
THE MOURNERS 96

subject: the arts

Selection 30 — Theme: Saying It through the Arts
KATHE KOLLWITZ 100

Selection 31 — Theme: Personalities in the Arts
PICASSO 103

CITIES OF THE FUTURE

ABOUT THE PASSAGE

During the twentieth century, American cities have become crowded, noisy areas, bare of grass and trees. Poisonous smells, wasteful use of water and electricity, and violence are ongoing problems. After experiencing these facts daily, many people are trying to change existing cities into healthful, attractive communities. Other people are planning totally new cities.

REASON FOR READING

To notice how the author organizes her information; to determine what techniques she uses to develop her ideas.

READ THE PASSAGE

The population of the world is increasing rapidly. By the year 2000 it is estimated there will be 8 billion people on earth, and what is more significant, 6.4 billion of these will live in cities. This trend toward city life has already had an impact on the major cities in our country, turning them into vast urban areas seething with humanity. They have spread and sprawled into the outlying suburbs, disrupting local community life. They have even merged into their neighboring cities.

Los Angeles is an extreme example of such growth. It is predicted that Los Angeles will eventually cover all the area for 450 miles, extending from Sacramento in the northern half of California to San Diego near the Mexican border.

The growth of Los Angeles has been irregular and disorganized, resulting in waste of space, materials, and time—and in a total lack of concern for the welfare of its inhabitants. It is crowded. There are slums and ugly industrial centers. Real estate developers have taken advantage of the situation, turning the natural beauty of the countryside into drab and shoddy residential compounds. The air is dirty; an umbrella of peculiar orange constantly hovers overhead. The water is impure and the transportation a nightmare. People have to travel such great distances and need to rely so much upon the automobile that approximately one eighth of the land is given to highways and functions connected with transportation, such as gas stations,

parking lots, and repair shops. Los Angeles, however, is not unique. Other major cities also display these undesirable characteristics.

The time has obviously come when we must remedy what is happening to our cities and assess how we can take care of the needs of the people while limiting the increase in their numbers. In addition to working within the cities as they already exist, we must create cities which provide the basic needs of life (housing, employment, services, and transportation) and also take into account the **intangible** human needs for space and freedom, for beauty and peace.

While the future of our cities is uncertain, several different approaches have been attempted and new ideas await testing. One approach to improving the city as it already exists has been for residents themselves to **renovate** the buildings and neighborhoods where they live. Usually this works best when there is a strong, interested leader living within the neighborhood. People in apartment buildings in New York and Boston have taken over management and care of both the outside and inside of their buildings. They have planted trees, flowers, and vegetables, cleaned the grounds, and worked together to protect their apartments from burglary. In Chicago and New York people have formed block associations in which they have joined together to care for their neighborhood, sharing their skills in the painting and repairing of their homes, making play areas, and limiting traffic. When people work together to improve where they already live, the sense of uselessness and defeat that ugly, noisy, violent surroundings creates, can disappear. Doing work that directly improves their own and their neighbors' lives has a good effect on how people feel toward each other and about themselves. This cooperative experience, more than the amount of money used, has determined the successful outcome of improved city housing.

Another approach taken has been to build new cities. The main feature of these cities is that they are based on total planning; all the **potential** problems are discussed and resolved before the actual building takes place. Housing, industries and businesses, recreational facilities, school systems, and the inevitable transportation problems are all considered in **conjunction** with one another. For example, ways are devised for children to walk safely to school without crossing streets, and for their parents to bicycle to work if they wish. **Communal** open spaces are provided to give a pleasing **aesthetic** appearance as well as to provide play areas. Different kinds of housing are available; there are apartments, townhouses, and homes for families. Many of these have communal heating and air-conditioning units which can be regulated according to each person's needs, but which reduce the costs considerably. In some cities the houses also have special television communication which allows the residents to shop from their homes or a neighbor to watch the children while parents are out.

Two of the most popular of these planned or "model" cities—Reston in Maryland and Columbia in Virginia—can be found on the outskirts of Washington, D.C., which actually was the first planned city in the nation. Washington was designed by a Frenchman named L'Enfant, who was given the task of changing the vast swamp it was then into the center of government and capital of the country. He worked out a carefully coordinated city plan based on an area ten miles square. Unfortunately, political squabbles, changes in personnel, and passing time disrupted and distroyed L'Enfant's initial plans.

Thus, although Washington remains one of the easiest cities to find your way around, it nevertheless has suffered all the same ills as other major cities.

With the development of new cities have come many new building and architectural ideas. One creative "revolutionizer of our environment," as he calls himself, is R. Buckminster Fuller. He has contributed such **innovative** ideas as **prefabricated**, moveable home units, which can be constructed quickly and easily and adapted according to the homeowner's changing needs. Fuller has also suggested an "Old Man River" project for East St. Louis which would consist of a domed, **autonomous**, tiered community to replace the city slums. Fuller is perhaps best known for the use of domes, especially his *geodesic* domes, in which triangles of material are connected in such a way that they can enclose vast areas. One such dome was used in the construction of the impressive United States pavilion at Expo '67 in Montreal. Fuller contends that the potential of his geodesic domes is limitless, and even suggests that whole cities could be constructed under them. Many applaud this idea as one way to combat the elements, but many others maintain they would get **claustrophobia** from never being able to see the sky or feel the wind, rain, or sun on their cheeks.

Two more of Fuller's concepts are "Triton City," a floating community for 100,000 persons, and a project for New York's Harlem district which could house 11,000 families in hundred-deck towers. Although neither of these has yet materialized, it is interesting to note that his ideas have been used in a waterside housing development on the East River in Manhattan. Taking ten years to develop, this project illustrates another trend in modern urban life—the city-within-a-city.

Waterside is built on more than 2,000 piles, some of which are driven as deep as 120 feet into the river to provide a platform covering most of the 67,000-square-foot site. It consists of 3 apartment towers of 37 stories each, 20 townhouse duplexes, a theater, restaurant, store, commercial space, and extensive community facilities. Waterside also illustrates a trend in the planning of future cities, by being what former New York mayor John Lindsay called "a fully economically integrated project," meaning that it provides homes for people of all income levels.

This is an especially important point, for as long as money from private firms rather than from the government finances these cities, the firms will plan and build housing and cities from which they can make a profit. They cannot make a profit from poor people who have a limited amount of money to spend. Consequently, they will plan cities for those who can pay—the middle- and upper-class people who already can buy adequate housing. A just and healthy society cannot come from such discrimination. Any plan for the city of the future needs to include healthy, clean, and restful housing for all people, not just those who can pay for it.

THINKING IT OVER

(1) What are some problems cities face? *Lack of adequate housing and transportation, too many cars, too much noise, very few trees or plants growing throughout the city, polluted air.*

(2) Which was the first planned city in the U.S.? *Washington, D.C.*

(3) Explain why it did or did not succeed. *The plan was not followed completely. Today, Washington has the same problems as other major cities.*

(4) What are the three main trends in new city developments? *(1) Improving cities as they already exist with residents taking responsibility for care of their neighborhoods; (2) development of new cities with total planning to provide for housing, employment, schools and recreation within easy reach for all; (3) creating projects that house a mixture of all economic groups.*

STUDYING THE PASSAGE

(1) Find the Main Idea: Choose one answer.
   (a) The growing population of our cities.
   (b) How we must change our cities.
   (c) The problems of our cities and how they might be overcome.
   (d) How new cities plan all aspects of life.   *c*

(2) Find the Facts: Mark each of these *true* or *false*.
   (a) The problems of Los Angeles are not unique.   (a) *T*
   (b) Cities need to include grass, trees, and space for recreation. (b) *T*
   (c) All aspects of life must be considered in city development.   (c) *T*
   (d) All the houses in the new cities have special television communication. (d) *F*
   (e) Washington, D.C. originally was developed on a 10-mile-square plan. (e) *T*
   (f) Problems of the city will not be solved if housing is created only for people who can pay for it. (f) *F*
   (g) Fuller created the geodesic dome.   (g) *T*
   (h) Money is the most important solution to the problems of cities. (h) *F*

(3) Find the Order: Number the following in the order in which they appear in the passage.

(a) When people work together to improve where they already live, the sense of uselessness and defeat can disappear.   (a) _4_

(b) A just and healthy society cannot come from such discrimination.   (b) _8_

(c) It is estimated there will be 8 billion people on earth in the year 2,000.   (c) _1_

(d) The cities have spread and sprawled into the outlying suburbs.   (d) _2_

(e) Fuller is a creative "revolutionizer of our environment."   (e) _7_

(f) Children can walk safely to school.   (f) _5_

(g) It was designed by a Frenchman named L'Enfant.   (g) _6_

(h) One eighth of the land is given to highways and functions connected with transportation.   (h) _3_

(4) Go beyond the Facts: Which two of the following conclusions may be drawn from the passage?

(a) Slums will be the major problem to eliminate from our cities.

(b) The ideas for new cities are stimulating many other innovative ideas.

(c) The writer suggests that cities are a serious problem that will not be solved quickly.

(d) The only way we can provide decent city life is to build entirely new cities.   _c_

(5) Determine the Writer's Style and Technique: Which one of the following is not included in the writer's description of American city life?

(a) An example of a city facing problems due to irregular, unorganized development.

(b) An example of a planned model city.

(c) An example of an actual city-within-a-city.

(d) An example of an individual who lives in one of the new cities.   _c_

(6) Words and Their Meanings: Find the boldface word which fits each of these definitions.

aesthetic   (a) of or pertaining to the beautiful

intangible   (b) that which cannot be touched or grasped

potential   (c) an adjective meaning "existing as a possibility, but not an actuality"; used as a noun to mean "future possibilities or prospects"

prefabricated   (d) made in advance; requiring only the assembly of preconstructed parts

conjunction   (e) combination, joining together

autonomous   (f) existing independently

innovative   (g) completely new; novel

communal   (h) pertaining or belonging to the people as a whole

renovate   (i) to make new again; to improve by repairing

claustrophobia   (j) extreme fear or dread of being in closed rooms or narrow spaces

4

COMMUNICATING WITH OUTER SPACE

ABOUT THE PASSAGE

The films *Star Wars*, *Close Encounters of a Third Kind*, and *2001: A Space Odyssey* are reflections of an old human curiosity about life in other parts of the universe. These films picture for our entertainment strange situations and unearthly experiences. In the future these experiences may be a familiar part of our human existence, for radio astronomy, a twentieth-century development, has been discovering details that make these seeming fictions appear closer to facts.

REASON FOR READING

To learn of the history and uses of radio astronomy.

READ THE PASSAGE

"At this instant, through this very document, radio waves may be passing, bearing the conversations of distant creatures, conversations that we could record if we but pointed a radio telescope in the right direction and tuned to the proper **frequency**." Not long ago this was the kind of thing you would read in science fiction or see portrayed in movies. But today you find it in the reports of such respected organizations as the Astronomy Survey Committee of the National Academy of Sciences.

Incredible as it seems, physicists and astronomers tell us there certainly is a possibility that creatures besides ourselves exist in the universe, and what is more, that we have the ability to make contact with them. Scientists have been able to make these remarkable statements mainly because of tremendous advances made during the last few decades in our communications systems.

In 1931 a young radio engineer for Bell Telephone Laboratories designed and constructed a large, rotating antenna. He wanted to determine the source of crackling **interference** in ship radio transmissions. What he discovered was that the sounds were regular signals or emissions from stars.

Gradually, other people became interested in this young man's work. During the last fifty years, extremely sophisticated and sensitive radio receivers have been developed. By using these, scientists have discovered certain **molecules** in **interstellar** space which are vital for life. By 1973 they had discovered twenty-three, some of which are water, ammonia, carbon monoxide, hydrogen cyanide, formaldehyde, and cyanogen. Now they are searching for five more (adenine, cytosine, guanine, tyrosine, and uracil) that comprise the vital nucleic acid which directs the development and reproduction of living cells. If they find these in reasonable quantities, it will make the argument for **extraterrestrial** life very persuasive, for it will indicate that exactly the same kind of chemistry that produced life on earth operates elsewhere in the universe.

The development of **ultra**sensitive telescopes, which is what the radio receivers are, was crucial to these discoveries, because only such instruments could pick up the radio waves which are given out by the molecules. One of the radio telescopes which contributed to much of this research is in Arecibo, Puerto Rico. Carved out of a natural limestone valley, it has a single disk measuring 1,000 feet in diameter and registers signals from billions of light years away. Another telescope is located at the University of California's observatory at Hat Creek. It was through this receiver that the signals of water and ammonia were detected. Some radio telescopes are engineered for distance and others for focusing power; still others are designed to receive signals in the very short (centimeter and millimeter) wave bands which chemical molecules usually **emit**.

Radio waves have specific usefulness for astronomers. They are one of the few kinds of waves that can penetrate the earth's atmosphere. While optical telescopes can be used only at night, radio receivers can gather information at any time. One serious problem for radio astronomy, however, is interference from a variety of sources—orbiting satellites above the earth or farmers' electrical fences, airports' radar beacons, and hospitals' diathermy machines on the earth.

If there were other beings in our universe, how would we make contact with them? Astronomers say this is easy—theoretically, at least. We would just do what any friendly neighbor might do—a little "eavesdropping." We would do this by using the radio telescope to pick up the radio signals they transmitted. These might be **unintentional** signals coming from radio and television broadcasts like our own or they might be actual messages deliberately sent by the creatures in an attempt to make contact with us.

When we do make contact with the creatures of the unknown, the next question will be, how do we carry on a conversation with them? Mathematicians tell us this is possible simply by transmitting coded arithmetic. They contend that all kinds of mathematical facts and formulas could be exchanged to establish a basic vocabulary for further communication. These would be transmitted in the form of organized sound patterns or "beeps." For example, "beep, beep-beep, beep-beep-beep" might signify "counting one, two, three."

The thought that there might be other living creatures in the universe and that we might actually be able to communicate with them is not quite so strange to people today. After all, most of us never imagined we would see one of our own kind walking about on the moon, did we?

THINKING IT OVER

(1) What have scientists found that makes them think there might be extraterrestrial life?

_____

(2) What else must they find in order to verify their assumptions? _____

_____

(3) What invention has enabled physicists and astronomers to collect this evidence? _____

_____

STUDYING THE PASSAGE

(1) Find the Main Idea: Choose one answer.
   (a) How we are making discoveries about interstellar life.
   (b) How we would communicate with creatures from outer space.
   (c) Discoveries that have been made about possible extraterrestrial life.
   (d) The possibility of other living beings existing in the universe, and how we would communicate with them.   _____

(2) Find the Facts: Mark each of these *true* or *false*.

  (a) By 1973, twenty-three molecules vital for life had been discovered in interstellar space.   (a) _____

  (b) Ammonia is vital for life.   (b) _____

  (c) Formaldehyde is a molecule which is part of nucleic acid.   (c) _____

  (d) The radio telescope in Puerto Rico has a diameter of 1,000 feet.   (d) _____

  (e) This radio telescope registers signals from billions of light years away.   (e) _____

  (f) "Eavesdropping," in astronomical language, is receiving radio signals.   (f) _____

  (g) The first radio telescope was constructed in the early 1800s.   (g) _____

  (h) Mathematicians say it would be easy to communicate mathematical facts and formulas to creatures in outer space.   (h) _____

(3) Find the Order: Number the following in the order in which they appear in the passage.

  (a) Only such instruments could pick up the radio waves which are given out by the molecules.   (a) _____

  (b) Some radio telescopes are engineered for distance.   (b) _____

  (c) Another one is located at the University of California's observatory.   (c) _____

  (d) He discovered that the sounds came from the stars.   (d) _____

  (e) We would just do what any friendly neighbor might do.   (e) _____

  (f) They are searching for five more molecules.   (f) _____

  (g) A serious problem for radio astronomy is interference from orbiting satellites.   (g) _____

  (h) We could "eavesdrop" by using the radio telescope to pick up radio signals.   (h) _____

(4) Go beyond the Facts: Which two conclusions does this article suggest?

  (a) The ideas and speculations of science fiction frequently remain fiction.

  (b) If living creatures were discovered in outer space, their alphabet might consist of numbers instead of letters.

  (c) Life on earth is a very small portion of the activity in the universe.

  (d) No radio telescope has been developed that is powerful enough to receive the radio signals from possible interstellar beings.   _____ _____

(5) Determine the Writer's Style and Technique: Which topic does the writer not include in the development of the article?

  (a) Some of the history of radio astronomy.

  (b) Details about research on the composition of living cells.

  (c) Explanation of how we could detect signals from extraterrestrial creatures.

  (d) Description of the way radio telescopes work.   _____

(6) Words and Their Meanings: Find the boldface word which fits each of these definitions.

_____   (a) relating to the universe or outer space; literally, the space between the stars

_____   (b) existing or originating outside the earth's atmospheric limits

_____   (c) in harmonic motions, the number of vibrations or cycles in a unit of time

_____   (d) to send out or give off

_____   (e) a hindrance or obstacle; something that blocks or prevents.

_____   (f) units of matter; the smallest portions of elements or compounds that retain their chemical identity

_____   (g) not done by design; accidental

_____   (h) going beyond others; extreme

Selection 3 — Subject: Combined Subjects
Theme: Transportation

SOME NEW WAYS TO MOVE

ABOUT THE PASSAGE
People have always moved from one place to another. For a long time this was done slowly on foot or in vehicles drawn by animals. With the development of cars propelled by engines, people enjoyed traveling great distances quickly and comfortably. But the great number of these vehicles has brought problems of crowded, polluted, unsafe, and noisy thoroughfares. Many people are seeking solutions to these problems.

REASON FOR READING
To understand what the problems are and to learn about different ideas for solving them.

READ THE PASSAGE

In the twentieth century the use of private, gasoline-powered cars began. For many years these seemed the ultimate luxury, but this convenient, comfortable, fast, private way of moving from one place to another became almost a curse as **congested**, foul-smelling expressways became commonplace during rush-hour traffic. Throughout the last decade the increasing cost of fuel to run cars, buses, and trucks has become a problem. People know that the total world supply of petroleum, which provides gasoline, is being **depleted** at such a rapid pace that little will be left by the year 2000. Since it took millions of years under special conditions to form these reserves, petroleum is considered a nonrenewable energy source. Clearly, it is time to seek other fuels and explore other ways of moving from place to place, ending our dependence on private automobiles and their transportation which requires nonrenewable resources, such as petroleum and coal.

Some ideas for change begin with the car itself. These include building more **efficient** engines. One design of increasing interest is the rotary engine, named the *Wankel* for its German inventor. Another is a stratified-charge engine developed in Japan. Yet another possibility is an electric car. Small private electric cars were once driven in the early 1900s, and New York City had electric taxi service in 1898. But electric cars were replaced when gasoline vehicles could travel longer distances at greater speeds. Now, engineers are trying to overcome the disadvantages of the electric car.

Another approach to solving the problem is in seeking new fuels. One possible alternative fuel is methane. This is a natural gas found in coal mines. It is formed by decaying plant and animal matter which is very plentiful. Methane can also be produced from sewage, the disposal of which is often a major problem for large cities. By converting sewage to methane fuel, it is possible that two serious problems could be solved at the same time.

People are changing their present driving habits. Some are driving to the edge of urban or metropolitan areas where buses, trains, or subways carry them to downtown jobs. Car pooling, too, is being used. In two months one radio station in a large city received more than 500,000 applications in response to its offer of a pooling service. Each driver received the names of ten potential passengers. The aim was to have a minimum of three people in a car in order to remove at least two cars from the road, their pollutants included, and to save gas.

But if people are to be less dependent on the car, the development of strong systems of public transportation is necessary. Some of the things people want from such systems are protection from weather while waiting, speed, frequent service, safety, adequate seating, and privacy. Including these qualities in a transportation system for any large or **sprawling** city like Los Angeles requires careful, thorough planning of the movement of buses, subways, and rapid transit trains, as well as pedestrians.

Of the ideas now being considered, one is a personal rapid transit system. This would consist of small cabs holding four to six passengers. The cabs would be easy for all people to enter, including those in wheelchairs, and those with bundles or with baby strollers. People could simply punch their destinations into a computer and then the automated cab could move them there within a few minutes. A computer center would control the entire system. The personal rapid transit would obviously be most effective in **urban** centers.

Other possibilities of moving from one place to another are systems that would transport people from one level to another as well as along lengthy airport corridors, where such systems are already in use. **Automated** highways to replace some of the present expressways are another idea. Cars would be hooked electronically to a buried cable and then would be moved to the desired destination. Since the cars would be controlled by a computer, they could be closer together and moving faster than when **manually** operated. Passengers, on the other hand, would arrive at their destinations without the **fatigue** and strain that accompany driving long distances.

While these last several suggestions are still being planned, budgeted, and debated, many people are already using another form of transportation that is pollution free, quiet, efficient, and inexpensive: the bicycle. With this vehicle, people avoid traffic jams, waiting in gas lines, and at the same time benefit from exercise.

While none of these ideas alone will provide a solution to our present transportation problems, together they can provide a beginning and perhaps stimulate new thinking and new ideas. But for each community to look at its own needs and then choose solutions that make use of many, all, or a few of these suggestions may be just what is needed to change travel into a quiet, comfortable, safe, yet efficient way of moving from one place to another—something that has been possible in the past only when people walked.

THINKING IT OVER

(1) What are some of the advantages of using the automobile? _____

_____

(2) What are some of the problems created by using the automobile? _____

_____

(3) In what ways are people changing their driving habits? _____

_____

STUDYING THE PASSAGE
(1) Find the Main Idea: Choose one answer.
   (a) Improving the efficiency of the gasoline engine.
   (b) Exploring the use of methane as fuel.
   (c) Finding safe, quiet, fast, clean ways of moving from one
       place to another.
   (d) Solving the problems of congested highways.   _____

(2) Find the Facts: Mark each of these *true* or *false*.
   (a) Oil resources, if used at the present rate, could be gone by the year 2000. (a) _____
   (b) Oil is a renewable resource. (b) _____
   (c) Bicycles are a nonpolluting, quiet way of traveling. (c) _____
   (d) Electric cars first appeared in New York City in the mid-twentieth century. (d) _____
   (e) Methane is formed from decaying plant and animal matter. (e) _____
   (f) People use car pools to save gas. (f) _____
   (g) Developing strong mass transportation systems is an important part of solving the problems of congested highways. (g) _____
   (h) One advantage of the automobile is its great safety. (h) _____

(3) Find the Order: Number the following in the order in which they appear in the passage.
   (a) It is time to seek other fuels and explore other ways of moving from place to place. (a) _____
   (b) People are changing their driving habits. (b) _____
   (c) Interest in the Wankel rotary engine is increasing. (c) _____
   (d) There is no single solution to the problems of transportation. (d) _____
   (e) People want their transportation to be fast, safe, comfortable, and private. (e) _____
   (f) The total world supply of petroleum is being depleted. (f) _____
   (g) Making methane fuel from sewage might help solve two serious problems. (g) _____
   (h) A strong public transportation system in cities is necessary. (h) _____

(4) Go beyond the Facts: Which one of the following conclusions may be drawn from the passage?
   (a) People would have been better off if the automobile had never been invented.
   (b) The most important step to solving transportation problems is finding a way of building cars that use a nonrenewable fuel.
   (c) People are more interested in their own comfort and convenience while traveling than in the wellbeing of everyone.
   (d) Changing just one thing in how people move from place to place will not solve the problems of transportation. _____

(5) Determine the Writer's Style and Technique: The main purpose of the author's discussion of transportation problems is:
   (a) To identify those who caused the problems.
   (b) To point out some possible solutions to a complex problem.
   (c) To explain her solutions for the problem.
   (d) To urge people to a solution she knows will work. _____

(6) Words and Their Meanings: In the passage find the boldface word which fits each of these definitions.

_____   (a)   spreading or developing irregularly

_____   (b)   tiredness, weariness

_____   (c)   effective in causing or producing

_____   (d)   clogged; concentrated in a small or narrow space

_____   (e)   run by a self-regulating mechanism

_____   (f)   having to do with the city

_____   (g)   involving the hands

_____   (h)   emptied; used up

MOTHER'S DAY

ABOUT THE PASSAGE

In many societies, women have often thought of motherhood as their appropriate and only work choice; in the last century this view has slowly changed. Many women are choosing to take other work in addition to the care of raising children. Some women are choosing not to have children. Nevertheless, Mother's Day continues to flourish. This is not surprising since changing, broadening women's roles have added to our concept of who and what a mother is.

REASON FOR READING

To notice the kinds of information the author includes about Mother's Day.

READ THE PASSAGE

Little by little women have been winning their rights. The **momentum** of law has gradually shifted to support their **aspirations** so that now, discrimination based on sex is **waning**. Today a woman can demand equal salary and equal consideration for all kinds of jobs: electrician, auto mechanic, lawyer, truckdriver. She is assigned sea duty if she is in the navy; if in the army, she is entitled to any job except direct combat positions. She is capable of playing as important a part in society as her fellow (male) human beings and is now running businesses, voting on boards of large corporations, or running for political office.

At home her role is also changing. She is no longer considered the one who must stay at home to do the housework, look after the kids, and prepare the meals. In many households the man changes the baby's diaper, regularly takes his turn at the stove, and does the weekly shopping at the grocery. On the other hand, it is often the woman who mows the lawn, repairs the faucet, builds shelving, changes the car's oil—jobs which were once considered the sole responsibility of the man.

And yet despite these changes and the new **perception** of the woman's role in American society today, there remains one day in the year when she is honored for the primary role she formerly was expected to take—Mother's Day.

There are many indications that Mother's Day is increasing in popularity rather than declining. Why should it continue to have so much appeal? No one knows for sure, but popular it is. For example, **restaurateurs**, card manufacturers, and stores report that their clients and sales increase annually. Many restaurateurs even **contend** it is their busiest day of the year, surpassing Christmas, Hanukkah, or New Year's.

The enthusiasm for Mother's Day is all the more remarkable when you consider it did not even become official in the United States until 1914. Contrary to many beliefs, it did not originate in America, nor was it developed by merchandisers purely as a commercial enterprise. The tradition began in England in the late 1400s, when young people were given a special holiday from their **apprenticeships** to return to their home towns and churches to observe a mid-Lenten Sunday. Then it was called "going a–mothering," for the apprentices would take gifts for their mothers and their mothers' churches.

Ancient civilizations, too, have honored mothers. They worshipped motherhood in the form of a goddess who encouraged the birth and growth of humans, plants, and other living things; or they acknowledged a special deity as a symbol of Mother Earth. For the Assyrians, this was Ishtar; for the Greeks, Demeter; and for the Romans, Ceres.

Mother's Day was first suggested as an American celebration in 1872 by Julia Ward Howe, who thought there should be a day dedicated to peace. However, it was not until 1907 that much interest was shown. In this year a Pennsylvania woman, Anna Jarvis, who had had her Sunday school classes make gifts for their mothers and write a special Mother's Day church service, started a campaign for nationwide observance of the day. She chose the second Sunday in May and began the custom of wearing a carnation. It is said that this custom was established in memory of President William McKinley, who always wore a white carnation in remembrance of his mother. Today some people wear a pink carnation for a living mother and a white one for a deceased mother.

Gradually more families **endorsed** Mother's Day and more churches introduced a special service on this day. By 1912 practically every state had set aside a special day to honor mothers. It was President Woodrow Wilson who gave the day official national recognition. On May 10, 1914, he issued a **proclamation** directing officials to display our flag as "a public expression of our love and reverence for the mothers of our country." He also stated that the day would always fall on the second Sunday in May.

Many people contend that Mother's Day has become too commercialized and has lost its original meaning. Nevertheless, it seems that Mother's Day is and will remain very much part of the American way of life in spite of the changes that are taking place in our society.

THINKING IT OVER

(1) Is Mother's Day a uniquely American tradition? Explain. _____

_____

(2) What are some jobs women do now along with or instead of being mother? _____

_____

_____

(3) Why is Mother's Day still so popular? _____

_____

STUDYING THE PASSAGE

(1) Find the Main Idea: Choose one answer.
    (a) Mother's Day is a national holiday.
    (b) Mother's Day is not a popular holiday.
    (c) Mother's Day continues as a time to honor mothers.
    (d) Mother's Day began with "going a-mothering" in earlier times. _____

(2) Find the Facts: Mark each of these *true* or *false*.
    (a) Women in the navy can now go to sea. (a) _____
    (b) The sale of Mother's Day cards increases annually. (b) _____
    (c) The tradition of Mother's Day began in the times of the
        Greeks and Romans. (c) _____
    (d) Anna Jarvis was the first person to try to establish Mother's
        Day as a nationally observed holiday. (d) _____

(e) President McKinley proclaimed Mother's Day a national day. (e) _____

(f) Mother's Day falls on the second Sunday in May. (f) _____

(g) Mothering is still an essential job. (g) _____

(h) Demeter was a mother goddess of the Greeks. (h) _____

(3) Find the Order: Number the following in the order in which they appear in the passage.

(a) Apprentices used to "go a-mothering." (a) _____

(b) Why should Mother's Day remain so popular? (b) _____

(c) Ancient civilizations honored mothers too. (c) _____

(d) Contrary to many beliefs, Mother's Day did not originate in America. (d) _____

(e) Anna Jarvis had her Sunday school classes make gifts for their mothers and write a special Mother's Day church service. (e) _____

(f) Many women chose not to be mothers and many mothers chose to do other work as well. (f) _____

(g) Many people contend Mother's Day has become too commercialized. (g) _____

(h) Women are running businesses, are on boards of large companies, and are active in the political arena. (h) _____

(4) Go beyond the Facts: Choose one. The writer can be described as:

(a) Sympathetic to the change in women's roles.

(b) Skeptical about the benefit of the variety of jobs now open to women.

(c) Opposed to too much emphasis on women as mothers.

(d) Concerned that some women choose not to be mothers. _____

(5) Determine the Writer's Style and Technique: Choose one. What kind of information does the author *not* include in the essay?

(a) Historical details about Mother's Day.

(b) Opinions of why the holiday is still popular.

(c) Personal experiences of a mother.

(d) Facts about how women's roles have changed. _____

(6) Words and Their Meanings: In the passage find the boldface word which fits each of these definitions.

_____ (a) to maintain or assert

_____ (b) strong hopes, wishes; ambitions

_____ (c) fading, diminishing

_____ (d) awareness of; consciousness

_____ (e) a public and official announcement

_____ (f) periods of service to learn a trade, taking usually from two to seven years

_____ (g) gave one's name in support; spoke for or recommended

_____ (h) force of motion in a particular direction; impetus

_____ (i) owner or operator of a restaurant

THE ALOHA STATE

ABOUT THE PASSAGE Hawaii, the fiftieth state of the United States, is the only one that is an island. Though a state for only a few decades, it has a rich and varied history that extends into the past more than a thousand years.

REASON FOR READING To learn of the history and economy of the Hawaiian people.

READ THE PASSAGE

When Captain Cook landed in the Hawaiian Islands in 1778, he was looking for the Northwest Passage between Europe and Asia. Instead he found islands inhabited by strong, brown people with straight or wavy black hair.

Who were these people? And how did they get there? It is generally believed that the Hawaiians, like other Polynesians, had their origins in Asia and were of mixed **Caucasian** and Mongolian descent. By 3,000–2,000 B.C. their ancestors were moving through Malaya, Indonesia, and the Philippines, intermarrying with the brown-skinned inhabitants of those areas. There was gradual eastward migration for over a hundred generations to more distant, uninhabited Pacific islands. The people probably reached Hawaii by way of Tahiti around A.D. 750.

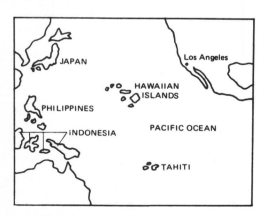

No one knows why they left Tahiti, but we do know that in order to reach Hawaii they had to navigate 2,500 miles of **uncharted**, unknown

ocean in their large outrigger canoes, which carried pigs, dogs, and chickens as well as sixty to a hundred people. No wonder they have been called the Vikings of the Pacific!

The main occupations of the Hawaiians, as they came to call themselves, were hunting and fishing. They worked hard, cultivating small fields on the slopes of the volcanoes, which they irrigated with care. In these fields they grew *taro*, a starchy, nutritious **tuber**. This they pounded and mixed with water, making a substance called "poi." Prepared with fish, this was their main diet, though they also grew yams, sugar cane, and breadfruit. The pigs that had come with them on their long journey ran wild all over the islands.

For celebrations the people organized pig-hunts, which **culminated** in a feast, highlighted by music and the dancing of the hula in a variety of ways. The Hawaiians were quite fond of music and had a range of string and **percussion** instruments.

Women had other special tasks. They stripped the bark off the mulberry trees, soaked it in water, and then beat it into strips. This "tapa" cloth was stamped with designs in brilliant colors. The dyes were made from the juices of fruits and nuts, and the designs were stamped on with bamboo rods. But perhaps most beautiful of all the Hawaiian creations were the elaborate feather cloaks and helmets, made from thousands of tiny feathers taken from small birds. The people were careful not to destroy the

16

source of their feathers; they did not kill the birds. Instead, a few feathers were taken from each one and then it was allowed to fly away.

Although the Hawaiians had no written language, their soft and musical spoken language had a vocabulary of over 20,000 words. They were fond of talking and of listening to history, folklore, stories, and legends, and carefully preserved these from one generation to the next by word of mouth.

Surrounded by a rich variety of plants, animals, fish, and birds, these people worshipped nature gods. There was Kane, the god of light; Lono, the god of harvest; Ku, the god of war; and most terrible of all, Pele, the goddess of the volcanoes. When Pele was angry the mountains spouted fire and red-hot stones. There was also Kanaloa, the ruler of the departed spirits.

For Captain Cook the discovery of the island paradise brought about, in a year's time, his own death through a scuffle with some islanders on a return trip. For the inhabitants, Cook's "discovery" of them brought a mixture of harmful and beneficial influences. Strangers—Haoles, as the islanders called them—came across the long stretches of ocean which for hundreds of years had **isolated** the Hawaiian people from the rest of the world. These "civilized" strangers from western countries such as America and France, brought with them not only religion, but rum; not only medicine, but disease. One result was that the population of the island was almost wiped out in the early nineteenth century. Within a short time, the number of native Hawaiians was halved.

Both sugar cane and pineapple have long been important crops for the Hawaiians. Contact with Europe and America, begun in the early nineteenth century, provided new markets. But gradually Hawaii needed more people to plant, and to care for and harvest those plants. Immigration from Portugal, Puerto Rico, China, and Japan was encouraged throughout the nineteenth century. The Hawaiians welcomed and intermarried with new residents, and the result is the striking mixture of people living in Hawaii today relatively free of racial problems.

In the late nineteenth century Hawaii and the United States made a significant trade agreement. The United States would buy large quantities of sugar and pineapple and Hawaii would purchase its food and other needs from the U.S. Soon almost all of the **arable** land was covered by huge sugar cane and pineapple plantations. Labor-saving devices and other **mechanization** in the production of both sugar and pineapple made these crops into major industries for Hawaii.

During the last fifty years Hawaii has experienced many changes. With increased mechanization, plantation work decreased as a source of employment. By the seventies the major sources of income for many Hawaiians were government work and the tourist industry. Problems of transportation (increased use of the car and no mass transit), concentration of jobs and the crowding of population on one island at the expense of others, and pollution of coastal fishing waters are serious concerns of Hawaiians. Already dependent on the United States for tourists and for a market for their crops, Hawaii permanently cemented that tie in 1959. After more than fifty years as a United States territory, Hawaii became the fiftieth state. Known as the Aloha State (*aloha* is a Hawaiian word for friendship), Hawaiians have welcomed many visitors from other countries.

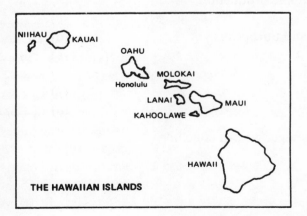

THE HAWAIIAN ISLANDS

THINKING IT OVER

(1) Why have the Hawaiians been called the Vikings of the Pacific? _____

_____

(2) What do the occupations of the early Hawaiians tell you about the kind of people they were?

_____

(3) How do Hawaiians feed themselves in the twentieth century? _____

_____

STUDYING THE PASSAGE

(1) Find the Main Idea: Choose one answer.
- (a) The story of a sea voyage.
- (b) The making of a state.
- (c) Settlement and change in Hawaii.
- (d) Hawaii's people.   _____

(2) Find the Facts: Mark each of these *true* or *false*.
- (a) Captain Cook landed in Hawaii by mistake.   (a) _____
- (b) Polynesian voyagers reached Hawaii around A.D. 750.   (b) _____
- (c) "Poi" was made from ground-up fish.   (c) _____
- (d) The hula dance is a fairly modern Hawaiian dance.   (d) _____
- (e) The women made cloth out of the bark of trees.   (e) _____
- (f) The Hawaiians had no written language.   (f) _____
- (g) Sugar cane, pineapples, and taro grow in Hawaii.   (g) _____
- (h) Sugar cane, pineapples, and tourism provide income to Hawaiians. (h) _____

(3) Find the Order: Number the following in the order in which they appear in the passage.
- (a) They worked hard cultivating small fields on the slopes of the volcanoes.   (a) _____
- (b) They were stricken by disease.   (b) _____
- (c) Labor-saving devices made sugar and pineapple production major industries.   (c) _____
- (d) They intermarried with Japanese, Chinese, and Europeans.   (d) _____
- (e) Haoles visited the island.   (e) _____
- (f) They navigated 2,500 miles of uncharted sea.   (f) _____
- (g) Hawaiians first came from Asia.   (g) _____
- (h) Hawaii became a state in 1959.   (h) _____

(4) Go beyond the Facts: Choose one. From the passage, we can conclude that the first "civilized" visitors to Hawaii:
- (a) Brought great prosperity to the islands.
- (b) Civilized the Hawaiians.
- (c) Harmed the Hawaiians' own civilization.
- (d) Tried to learn from the Hawaiians' civilization.   _____

18

(5) Determine the Writer's Style and Technique: Choose one. The writer tells us about the Hawaiians by:
    (a) Giving vivid descriptions.
    (b) Giving facts and details.
    (c) Telling stories about them.
    (d) Using comparisons.   _____

(6) Words and Their Meanings: In the passage find the boldface word which fits each of these definitions.

_____   (a) removed from contact with others; separated

_____   (b) fit for cultivation

_____   (c) completed, ended; reached the highest point

_____   (d) the striking or beating of an object

_____   (e) people with light, pale skins

_____   (f) equipping with machinery to replace human labor

_____   (g) not on the map; unexplored

_____   (h) a swollen, underground stem, such as the potato

CIVIL RIGHTS

ABOUT THE PASSAGE

Though the Civil War was fought in the 1860s to abolish slavery and unequal treatment of blacks, more than a hundred years later unequal treatment because of color still persists. Along with the continuous efforts of innumerable people through that hundred years, two men, one black and one white, added their actions to the fight for equality of all people.

REASON FOR READING

To notice how the author builds the image of each of these men.

READ THE PASSAGE

Few in the audience realized that he was living on borrowed time. Admittedly he was twenty pounds leaner and his rugged face was furrowed with lines of fatigue; but then, they all were tired from the unusually long and hazardous journeys which the ice-storm had caused.

Few realized what a toll his four-hour journey to Austin had taken, and how his attendance at the meetings the day before and the evening reception for a thousand guests had overwhelmed him with a tiredness that only the dying can know. Few knew of the night he had spent engulfed in pain and of the doctors' pleas for him not to go through with this speech. All they knew was that this was the man they had grown to respect—who had done much for their cause.

It was December, 1972. The occasion was a **symposium** at the Lyndon Baines Johnson Library at the University of Texas, and the participants were listening to L.B.J. himself speaking on a subject which had been uppermost in their minds for the last two decades: **civil rights**.

Johnson talked for twenty minutes. His voice was low and steady, but even in this short time the pain in his chest became so great he had to reach **surreptitiously** for one of his nitroglycerin tablets. His speech, however, was **eloquent** and to the point: "Until we overcome unequal history we cannot overcome unequal opportunity," he said. "But to be black in a white society is not to stand on equal and level ground. While the races may stand side by side, whites stand on history's

mountain and blacks stand in history's hollow. . . . So I think it is time to leave aside the legalisms and **euphemisms** and eloquent evasions. It's time we get down to the business of trying to stand black and white on level ground."

When he finished he stepped down from the stage amid loud applause to resume his seat beside a worried Lady Bird Johnson. She knew what that twenty minutes had cost. But this was not to be his final contribution to the meeting. Soon afterwards, arguments broke out among some of the factions in the audience and a serious confrontation seemed about to take place. Sensing this, Johnson moved to save the situation. Once again he was on the stage, counseling and helping to find a compromise, as he had often done in his Senate days. He told them to talk together, to "just cool and push off wrath, indulge, tolerate and finally come out with a program of objectives." He ended with some words that have lingered in many of his audience's memories since: "While I can't provide much go–go at this period in my life, I can provide a lot of hope and dream and encouragement."

And that is what this rugged, courage-filled Texan had done for civil rights; he had provided a lot of hope, a lot of dream, and a lot of encouragement. In his earlier years, he had also contributed more than his share of "go–go."

It was his energy and endless persistence when he was the Senate Majority Leader that led to the first new Civil Rights Act in eighty-two years. Through endless public speeches and quiet, behind-the-scenes conversations with key politicians, he worked to persuade people of the need for reform. Above all, he was willing to spend time with the ordinary persons of any skin color, in order to achieve equal rights.

In his 1965 civil rights address to Congress, President Johnson quoted the **poignant** refrain, "We shall overcome." He considered the Voting Rights Act passed that year to be the greatest accomplishment of his administration. With greatly increased voter registration, the number of blacks elected to state and local offices had increased from some 70 to almost 400 by 1968. By 1978, the number of blacks holding elected offices was 4,503.

Johnson also appointed the first black to the Supreme Court. Born the same year as Johnson, this man, Thurgood Marshall, in many ways had led a very different life from Johnson's, but like Johnson had spent much of his life fighting for civil rights.

Marshall worked extremely hard and reached the **pinnacle** of his profession. He had attended Howard University Law School, where he was graduated first in his class, but had waited on tables and bellhopped to earn money for the tuition. After law school he set up his own law practice in Baltimore. Here his clients were almost always poor people. Their legal problems usually concerned **eviction**, repossession of goods, and police brutality. His hard work on the preparation of these cases and his careful, precise, and objective arguments won him both the cases and the respect of his opponents. He has said that it was in Baltimore that he truly learned what civil rights were. In the process, he became one of the greatest constitutional lawyers of this century.

From his practice in Maryland, Marshall constructed a legal **arsenal** for civil rights which made him the most feared **antagonist** in the Southern courts. For twenty-three years, he served as legal counsel for the NAACP (National Association for the Advancement of Colored People), and during this time established the rights of blacks in the South to vote, to serve on juries, and to go to integrated public schools. Out of thirty-two cases he argued before the Supreme Court he won twenty-nine. In 1954 he was the attorney who successfully argued before the Court that racial segregation in public schools was unconstitutional. This was the historic *Brown* v. *Board of Education* case. The court said "separate but equal" educational facilities did *not* provide people with equal protection and due process under the law.

Marshall was one of many blacks who filled influential positions during Johnson's administration. In addition, there were such men as Walter Washington, who became the first mayor of Washington, D.C. in 1967, and Dr. Robert Weaver, the first black Cabinet member, who headed the new Department of Housing and Urban Development.

THINKING IT OVER

(1) What did Johnson and Marshall have in common? _____

_____

(2) How did they differ? _____

_____

STUDYING THE PASSAGE

(1) Find the Main Idea: Choose one answer.

    (a) Johnson did more for civil rights than any other president.

    (b) A Southerner fights for civil rights.

    (c) The contributions made to civil rights by two men.

    (d) How Johnson gave his life for civil rights.   _____

(2) Find the Facts: Mark each of these *true* or *false*.

    (a) Johnson was in much pain during the symposium.   (a) _____

    (b) The symposium was held in January.   (b) _____

    (c) Johnson's speech caused arguments.   (c) _____

    (d) Marshall and Johnson didn't know each other.   (d) _____

    (e) Johnson brought about the first Civil Rights Act to be passed by Congress in eighty-two years.   (e) _____

    (f) Marshall was the first black appointed to the Supreme Court.   (f) _____

    (g) Marshall became the beloved protagonist in the Southern courts.   (g) _____

    (h) Johnson and Marshall were the same age.   (h) _____

(3) Find the Order: Number the following in the order in which they appear in the passage.

    (a) Soon afterwards arguments broke out.   (a) _____

    (b) He felt that the Voting Rights Act was his administration's greatest achievement.   (b) _____

    (c) Dr. Robert Weaver was the first black cabinet member.   (c) _____

    (d) Thurgood Marshall had spent much of his life fighting for civil rights.   (d) _____

    (e) This was the historic *Brown* v. *Board of Education* case.   (e) _____

    (f) He had provided a lot of hope and dream and encouragement.   (f) _____

    (g) He became one of the greatest constitutional lawyers of the century.   (g) _____

    (h) "It is time we get down to the business of trying to stand black and white on level ground."   (h) _____

(4) Go beyond the Facts: Choose two. It seems correct to conclude from this selection that:

    (a) It took Thurgood Marshall a long time to learn what civil rights really were.

    (b) The direction of the Supreme Court has shifted radically since Marshall became a member.

    (c) Americans have been eager to end inequality of treatment wherever they see it.

    (d) Both black and white people have worked to stop unequal and unfair treatment of blacks.   _____ _____

(5) Determine the Writer's Style and Technique: The author uses two different styles to describe the men in this passage. Which answer best identifies these two styles?

(a) Legend (Johnson); personal experience (Marshall).

(b) Narration of an experience (Johnson); listing of facts (Marshall).

(c) Impersonal and formal (Johnson); informal and emotional (Marshall).

(d) General biography (Johnson); personal anecdotes (Marshall). _____

(6) Words and Their Meanings: In the passage find the boldface word which fits each of these definitions.

_____ (a) the act of forcing tenants to vacate their quarters for nonpayment of rent or other reasons

_____ (b) emotionally moving, touching

_____ (c) a conference at which a particular subject is discussed

_____ (d) stealthily; in a concealing manner

_____ (e) economic, political, and social rights belonging to people because they are citizens of a country

_____ (f) adversary, opponent

_____ (g) a place for making and storing weapons

_____ (h) mild, inoffensive terms used to name things that might otherwise sound unpleasant, e.g. "passed away" for "died"

_____ (i) speaking smoothly, persuasively

_____ (j) highest point, greatest achievement

Selection 7 — Subject: Social Studies
Theme: How Others Live

A TRIP TO MOSCOW

ABOUT THE PASSAGE   Some of its buildings are over five hundred years old. Its subway system is famous for its speed and beauty. Many of its residents covet a pair of blue jeans and, if they get a pair, wear them to shreds. All of these details are true of Moscow, the capital of the largest nation on earth.

REASON FOR READING   To learn specific facts and descriptive details about this old city.

READ THE PASSAGE

Not long ago a good friend of mine returned from a trip to Russia. She is an excellent runner and had participated in a **prestigious** international competition. Although training and racing took up much of her time, Sarah took time to wander through Moscow to get a feeling for this old and impressive city. Eager to hear her descriptions, I invited her to come over one afternoon and tell me details of what she had seen. She agreed.

When she and her team were in Moscow they stayed in pleasant, twelve-story apartment buildings near the center of Moscow. Moscow, Sarah said, is a sprawling, circular city. This capital of the world's largest nation is a metropolis of 340 square miles and 8 million people. All of Russia's roads radiate from Moscow.

In the center is the Kremlin, the headquarters of the Communist party. Long ago this same spot was a small settlement on a hill above the **confluence** of two rivers. This became a walled fort in the mid-twelfth century. The Kremlin, which means "fortress," grew around this original settlement. It was surrounded by moats and drawbridges. The present red brick walls of the Kremlin were designed by architects in the fifteenth century and enclose palaces and churches built by the tsars, as well as the buildings of the Soviet government.

Beyond the Kremlin walls run two circular boulevards, one built in the sixteenth century and one in the seventeenth. A modern highway circles the city some ten miles from the Kremlin. The Moscow River, formerly a route of trade, flows in the center of the city. Nearby, the gentle slopes of the Lenin Hills make Moscow one of the few major cities with skiing facilities inside their city limits.

Red Square is the **hearthstone** of Russia. Here, in its mile-and-a-quarter expanse, huge military and civilian parades take place. Here special events are celebrated. Most visitors, however, come to Red Square to see Lenin's Tomb. The tomb lies near the main gates to the Kremlin, and from the Kremlin's gates a glowing red star pierces the evening light. Just beyond rise the onion-domes of the fairy-tale towers of St. Basil's Cathedral, built by Ivan the Terrible in 1552 to celebrate his victory over the Tartars.

Today, Sarah said, a trade center and huge hotel for tourists have been added to the palaces and other buildings lining the Moscow River. Moscow is changing each year, her Russian guides told her. Hundreds of new buildings are constructed, more automobiles travel the circular highways, and the standard of living has improved. Sarah saw people wearing blue jeans, a much desired item of clothing not available in Russian stores.

Satellite communities are being built around the edge of the city, often in places where old villages formerly stood. Villagers, however, are not upset as they watch the new twelve- to sixteen-story apartments being built, for these will have running water and heating. When the villagers move into their new quarters, they will appreciate the change from **stoking** coal stoves and collecting cold water from a stand pipe in the street.

Most buildings are heated by a central supply system feeding them steam through underground lines. Natural gas is the main fuel in Russia. It comes from central Asia and Siberia. Russia has one quarter of the world's natural gas reserves but nevertheless has **instituted** a widespread fuel conservation program. Since natural gas is a clean-burning fuel, there is little air pollution.

Moscow accounts for 7 percent of the industrial output of Russia, producing machine tools, motor vehicles, and electronic and precision instruments. One problem is a shortage of workers in every field. But at the same time Moscow planners want to control population growth. Moscow has a master plan for city development. To control the growth there are restrictions on moving to Moscow. Sarah's Russian guides told her that first a person must get a residence permit. To do this one must have a job. Next the employer needs to make a statement that the person is necessary. After this an individual waits until there is an apartment available.

Moscow has an excellent subway system, one of the best in the world. Its 102 miles of track are expected to be doubled by the year 2000. The stations are decorated with chandeliers, public bath ceramics, and **mosaic** sculptures. There are one-half mile escalators and a beehive of corridors that loom into sudden halls. And the trains are on time, Sarah said, leaving every 90 seconds during rush hour. Authorities plan to double the 102 miles of track by the year 2000. Moscow also has good bus and streetcar service.

Schooling and athletics are important to Muscovites. Eighty percent of children between two and six are enrolled in 2,149 kindergartens. **Ideology** is emphasized. Students are required to study the ideas of Marx and Lenin for at least ten years. There are regular schools as well as special ones for children with difficulties or talents. Of the special schools, many are for dance and gymnastics; Russians love and excel in both.

In winter, Sarah's Russian friends told her, the temperature may often be between —15° and —8°F. for weeks on end. Natural fur is one material that gives adequate warmth against this cold. People wear fur hats, fur coats, and fleece-lined boots when they **venture** out.

Sarah said she was glad she had missed winter in Moscow, but she had enjoyed her warm-weather stay. She thought seeing another way of life had been an interesting experience.

THINKING IT OVER

(1) Give three historic sights in Moscow. _____

_____

(2) Describe Moscow's subways. _____

_____

STUDYING THE PASSAGE

(1) Find the Main Idea: Choose one answer.
   (a) Russia—past and present.
   (b) Some facts and descriptions of Moscow.
   (c) Why travel is good for you.
   (d) The importance of international competitions.   _____

25

(2) Find the Facts: Mark each of these *true* or *false*.
    (a) The red brick Kremlin walls date to the fifteenth century.   (a) _____
    (b) The river which flows through Moscow is called the Moscow River.   (b) _____
    (c) Moscow is 45 square miles of sprawling city.   (c) _____
    (d) Lenin's Tomb nestles in the hills where people ski.   (d) _____
    (e) Nuclear power plants provide most of the fuel for Russia.   (e) _____
    (f) Getting from one place to another in Moscow doesn't
         take long by subway.   (f) _____
    (g) New apartment buildings have running water.   (g) _____
    (h) Education is valued by Muscovites.   (h) _____

(3) Find the Order: Number the following in the order in which they appear in the passage.
    (a) There is little air pollution.   (a) _____
    (b) Satellite communities are built around the edge of the city.   (b) _____
    (c) There are restrictions on moving to Moscow.   (c) _____
    (d) Students study the ideas of Marx and Lenin.   (d) _____
    (e) There are 102 miles of track in the subway system.   (e) _____
    (f) The Kremlin is in the center of Moscow.   (f) _____
    (g) Russia has one quarter of the world's reserves of natural gas.   (g) _____
    (h) Winter temperatures may often stay below 0°F. for weeks on end.   (h) _____

(4) Go beyond the Facts: Which conclusions are based on information given
in the passage? (Choose two.)
    (a) Moscow will probably encourage Western visitors.
    (b) American cities could learn from Moscow's subway system.
    (c) Moscow depends on trade for most of its goods.
    (d) Moscow is not located near the equator.   _____   _____

(5) Determine the Writer's Style and Technique: Which type of writing does
the author use?
    (a) Biography.
    (b) Autobiography.
    (c) Dramatization.
    (d) Personal account.   _____

(6) Words and Their Meanings: In the passage find the boldface word which fits each of these definitions.

_____ (a) risk the hazards of; proceed despite danger

_____ (b) stone forming the fireside of a home; hence the center of life

_____ (c) a usually independent urban community located near a large city

_____ (d) originated and got established; organized

_____ (e) honored; having prestige

_____ (f) a body of ideas and beliefs, especially about human life and culture

_____ (g) a coming or flowing together

_____ (h) a surface decoration made by inlaying small pieces of variously colored material to form pictures or patterns

_____ (i) poking or stirring up (as a fire); supplying with fuel

THE AMBIGUOUS ATOM

ABOUT THE PASSAGE

When scientists learned how to split the atom, they discovered an amazing and fearful source of energy. How to use this power in undestructive ways continues to be a perplexing problem.

REASON FOR READING

To follow an explanation of some issues involved with a complex problem.

READ THE PASSAGE

Almost everyone knows at least one use of atomic energy. Humans first used atomic energy to create the atomic bomb. Atomic bombs were dropped on Hiroshima and Nagasaki to help the **Allies** end World War II. Although the A-bomb caused a huge number of deaths and lasting injuries to many survivors, atomic energy need not be destructive. Many scientists believe it can be **beneficial** to society.

To understand **nuclear** energy, one must know how it is produced. Everything is made up of atoms which one cannot see. In the center of the atom is the nucleus, composed of protons and neutrons held together by a tight bond of nuclear energy. When the nuclear bond is broken, in a process called **fission**, this tremendous atomic energy is released.

A **nuclear reactor** is a device that is used as a source of heat in a nuclear power plant. It contains **radioactive** "fuel," uranium, in which fission occurs at a controlled rate. Uranium is a heavy element that is found in nature as a metal. Uranium 235, a form of this element, is the primary source of atomic energy. It has been found that only one pound of uranium can produce more energy than 1,300 tons of coal. One drawback, however, is that uranium is not a very abundant element.

During the 1950s and early 1960s, after the terrible destruction by the atomic bombs in Japan, people were eager to develop peaceful uses of nuclear power. Some of the hopes of these years were that power from the atom would

help provide cheap home electricity and would make a cleaner environment, since this fuel would not pollute the air as do oil and coal. The first nuclear plant for electricity was built by Westinghouse at Shippingsport, Pennsylvania in 1957. During the next decade at least another fifty nuclear power plants were constructed and several hundred more were planned. By 1970 1.3 percent of the nation's electricity came from nuclear power. It was hoped that by the 1980s 22 percent would be provided.

But problems occurred. The cost of uranium increased in these decades rather than decreased as engineers had expected. This drastically increased the cost of building and operating nuclear power plants. More serious, however, was the continuing and growing concern of people about the dangerous, radioactive fuel. People were fearful of radiation leaking from reactors into the soil and from there into community water supplies; they were concerned too about invisible leakage of radiation into the air.

Radiation is dangerous to humans. In large amounts it kills; in lesser amounts it can cause fatal and other diseases and gene **mutation**. Such mutation could alter the very nature of what is human.

In addition there was the fear of a major nuclear accident. One of the worst accidents that could happen would be a core meltdown. This means that something unpredictable would happen that would cause the water in the cooling jacket surrounding a reactor to be lost. The core

28

of the reactor would then melt into the ground and release clouds of radioactivity. Such an occurrence could cause tens of thousands of fatalities and injuries and make the land for miles around uninhabitable.

In March of 1979, at a power plant at Three Mile Island, Pennsylvania, a serious nuclear accident did happen. Although there was no loss of life, residents were evacuated from the area for two weeks, and even though all immediate danger was over within a month, the long-term effects of the breakdown still are not known.

Finally, people are concerned about what to do with the radioactive wastes produced by fission. The wastes remain radioactive (and consequently harmful or even deadly to human life) for thousands of years. Where or even how to store these wastes safely is a problem that some people say must be solved before we build great numbers of nuclear power plants.

While **proponents** say that nuclear energy is a logical and necessary solution to the dwindling supply of fossil fuels, opponents believe our lives and the lives of people in future generations would be endangered if nuclear power is used on a large scale before the serious problems connected with it are solved.

THINKING IT OVER

(1) How is nuclear energy produced? _____
_____

(2) What is a beneficial use of nuclear energy? _____
_____

(3) What are some of the problems with nuclear power plants? _____
_____
_____

STUDYING THE PASSAGE

(1) Find the Main Idea: Choose one answer.
    (a) The A-bomb was the most powerful bomb ever produced.
    (b) Atomic energy is produced when an atomic nucleus is split.
    (c) Researchers are constantly looking for new ways to use atomic energy.
    (d) While use of atomic energy for fuel may solve some serious problems, it causes additional, equally serious problems. _____

(2) Find the Facts: Mark each of these *true* or *false*.
    (a) Everything is made up of atoms.   (a) _____
    (b) Uranium 235 is the primary source of atomic energy.   (b) _____
    (c) Uranium is one of the more common elements in the earth's crust.   (c) _____
    (d) Nuclear power is cleaner than oil or coal.   (d) _____
    (e) Three Mile Island was where the first atomic bomb was tested.   (e) _____
    (f) Radioactivity is harmful to human life.   (f) _____
    (g) People have had great hopes that nuclear energy could be used in ways that would benefit human life.   (g) _____
    (h) Nuclear power plants are not expensive to build and operate.   (h) _____

(3) Find the Order: Number the following in the order in which they appear in the passage.

(a) Tremendous energy is released when the nucleus of the atom is broken apart.   (a) _____

(b) By 1970 1.3 percent of the nation's electricity came from nuclear power.   (b) _____

(c) A core meltdown is one of the worst nuclear accidents that could happen.   (c) _____

(d) Atomic bombs were dropped on Hiroshima and Nagasaki.   (d) _____

(e) Uranium is not very abundant.   (e) _____

(f) People were afraid their soil and water would become contaminated by radiation.   (f) _____

(g) Wastes remain radioactive for thousands of years.   (g) _____

(h) People were eager to develop peaceful uses of atomic energy.   (h) _____

(4) Go beyond the Facts: Choose one. From information in the passage, we could conclude that:

(a) Nuclear energy no longer is hazardous for people.

(b) Scientists will probably find solutions for most of the serious problems connected with using nuclear energy.

(c) We need to use nuclear energy because our natural sources of energy are rapidly being depleted.

(d) Nuclear energy can be of use to human beings, but we must use it with great caution.   _____

(5) Determine the Writer's Style and Technique: Choose one.

(a) Using facts to explain a line of reasoning.

(b) Using examples to show what something is.

(c) Telling a story to illustrate a fact.

(d) Comparing and contrasting to define something.   _____

(6) Words and Their Meanings: In the passage find the boldface word which fits each of these definitions.

_____   (a) parties joined together in a common fight; as a proper noun, those countries which fought against the Axis powers (Germany, Japan, Italy) in World War II

_____   (b) those who argue in favor of something

_____   (c) having to do with the nucleus, or center; atomic

_____   (d) the splitting of an atomic nucleus into two smaller nuclei

_____   (e) helpful

_____   (f) spontaneously giving off radiation, usually as a consequence of a nuclear reaction

_____   (g) sudden genetic changes which cause an offspring to show different characteristics from its parents

_____   (h) a device for splitting large numbers of atoms in a chain reaction

30

DIANA NYAD*

ABOUT THE PASSAGE   On August 20, 1979, Diana Nyad successfully swam from the Bahamas to Florida, a distance of sixty miles. But this was not her first record as a long distance swimmer. When she was twenty-four, she swam Lake Ontario in a way that no other swimmer had.

REASON FOR READING   To notice how the author uses descriptive details that help readers feel as though they are accompanying the swimmer.

READ THE PASSAGE

It takes at least fourteen hours to swim across Lake Ontario. Diana Nyad knew that, but didn't let it bother her. She is one of those rare persons known as a long-distance swimmer. They thrive on challenges—the harder, the better.

Diana wanted to do what no other swimmer had done before. She would try to swim across Lake Ontario starting from the Canadian side, the north shore. Swimmers have always started from the south shore because that's where the Niagara River empties into the lake. The push from the river current is a great help. Diana chose to do it the hard way.

She also would be the first to try to swim a round trip. She planned to cross the lake, rest for fifteen minutes and then swim back to where she had started.

Lake Ontario is a **rugged** test for swimmers. One of the coldest of the Great Lakes, it is called an inland sea because it is so big—thirty-two miles wide where Diana planned to cross it. The lake has tricky currents and waves that sometimes are as wild as an ocean's. Even the great long-distance swimmer, Florence Chadwick, the first ever to swim the **treacherous** English Channel in both directions, had failed to make it across Ontario.

Diana started at ten in the morning, wading into the lake at the Toronto waterfront. A group of reporters were there to see this twenty-four-year-old woman set out to do the impossible.

Four close friends were aboard the boat that accompanied her. They fed her cups of hot chocolate every hour. She felt strong, as if she could do anything. Years and years of serious training had prepared her well for this feat. For eight hours she stroked smoothly and steadily. Her pace was so fast the navigator said they would make it across in less than fourteen hours. Hooray, she thought. Her spirits soared.

But at the end of eight hours, problems started. The wind picked up. Soon she was heading into five-foot waves. The steady, strong **pace** became a **lunging** battle. She was using reserves she had hoped to save for the return trip. The fourteen hours they had all hoped for grew to fifteen, then sixteen, seventeen, and eighteen. Diana was shaking with cold and weak from the slapping waves. It was 4:00 A.M. and pitch-black when her trainer yelled for her to stop. He wanted to ask a question.

"What are you going to do once we reach shore?" he shouted.

"Take fifteen minutes rest and keep on going," the exhausted swimmer answered.

Twenty minutes later, off balance and freezing, she slowly made her way up the beach. She sank into a chair. Flashbulbs sparked. Reporters wanted to know her thoughts. Her trainer and friends tried to warm her a little by greasing her body.

"Those were the quickest fifteen minutes

*From *Women in Sports: Swimming*, by Diana G. Gleasner. © 1975. Harvey House. Reprinted by permission.

I've ever known," she remembers.

She put her goggles back on. After finally getting to solid ground and having a warm blanket around her, it was very hard to get up and walk into the water again.

"After eighteen hours of fighting that lake," she said, "the very last thing on earth I wanted to do was wade back into those icy depths. I knew I had at least fourteen hours of swimming ahead of me."

But Diana is not a quitter. She had come to do the impossible. And the impossible is never easy. Still, she couldn't stop shaking and she was tired beyond belief.

What kept her going? Diana explained, "It is frighteningly easy after eighteen hours of steady swimming through chilly, five-foot waves to lose confidence. It's easy to lose sight of why you wanted to attempt such a looney thing in the first place. But people I loved and respected were riding through those waves and bearing that cold and awful night with me. Somehow I would lift my arms again and again and again."

Diana's memory of that night was **vivid**. "Lake Ontario wasn't very good to me. In the short forty-five minutes it had taken to enter the harbor, rest, and swim back through the harbor, the wind had turned around. Now it was coming straight at me again. The waves were as tall as I was. I was determined to keep going. I remember rolling over about 5:30 A.M. and shouting, "We're going to make it!"

But the cold and exhaustion had taken their **toll**. At 6:30 A.M. after twenty hours and thirty minutes of lifting one arm after another, Diana lost consciousness.

The newspapers said Diana had "failed" because she hadn't completed the round trip. But she had been the only person ever to cross Lake Ontario from north to south. And the fact that she had kept going through the night, the cold, and the waves was a **tribute** to the superb **conditioning** of her mind and body. It was much more than an athletic feat to her.

"It was," she said, "the most intense experience of my life."

THINKING IT OVER

(1) In what two ways was Diana Nyad's attempt to swim Lake Ontario unlike any other swimmer's before her? _____

(2) What were some of the things that helped Diana keep going in spite of the terrible conditions? _____

_____

STUDYING THE PASSAGE

(1) Find the Main Idea: Choose one answer.
   (a) Diana Nyad's attempt to cross Lake Ontario.
   (b) How Diana failed to cross Lake Ontario.
   (c) How Diana succeeded in crossing Lake Ontario.
   (d) The slow way to cross Lake Ontario.   _____

(2) Find the Facts: Mark each of these *true* or *false*.
   (a) Diana expected to swim across Lake Ontario in fourteen hours.   (a) _____
   (b) Lake Ontario is one of the coldest of the Great Lakes.   (b) _____
   (c) Lake Ontario is called an inland sea because it is so big.   (c) _____
   (d) Ten close friends accompanied her.   (d) _____
   (e) Her friends gave her hot soup during the trip.   (e) _____
   (f) The wind was the main cause of her problems.   (f) _____
   (g) Diana was too exhausted to start the return trip.   (g) _____

(3) Find the Order: Number the following in the order in which they appear in the passage.

    (a)   I remember rolling over about 5:30 A.M. and shouting "We're going to make it!"   (a) _____

    (b)   Hooray, she thought. Her spirits soared.   (b) _____

    (c)   The very last thing on earth I wanted to do was wade back into the icy depths.   (c) _____

    (d)   It was 4:00 A.M. and pitch-black when her trainer yelled for her to stop.   (d) _____

    (e)   But the cold and exhaustion had taken their toll.   (e) _____

    (f)   Her trainer and friends tried to warm her a little by greasing her body.   (f) _____

    (g)   A group of reporters were there.   (g) _____

    (h)   It was much more than an athletic feat to her.   (h) _____

(4) Go beyond the Facts: Which one would best describe Diana Nyad?

    (a)   A diver.

    (b)   A speed swimmer.

    (c)   A marathon swimmer.

    (d)   A synchronized swimmer.   _____

(5) Determine the Writer's Style and Technique: Which two of the following does the writer do:

    (a)   Describes Diana Nyad's swimming career.

    (b)   Describes several incidents in her swimming career.

    (c)   Describes one incident in detail.

    (d)   Gives clues to Diana's personality.   _____ _____

(6) Words and Their Meanings: In the passage find the boldface word which fits each of these definitions.

_____   (a)   a state of fitness, readiness

_____   (b)   rough, harsh, difficult

_____   (c)   lively, fresh, intense

_____   (d)   a price or fee

_____   (e)   tempo or rate at which something is done

_____   (f)   something that shows the worth or effectiveness of a thing

_____   (g)   leaping, pushing forward

_____   (h)   dangerous

FOR THE GOOD OF HUMANITY

ABOUT THE PASSAGE   The use of nuclear power either for weapons and defense or for energy to run factories, to heat and light buildings is a controversial topic and a serious concern for all people. It can provide great benefits to human beings, but at the same time it is one of the most dangerous threats to all life on earth if it is not carefully produced, used, and disposed of.

REASON FOR READING   To consider the effects when one large country does things that benefit it but harm smaller countries; to think about who should make the decisions about the use of nuclear energy and what is meant by the phrase "for the good of humanity."

READ THE PASSAGE

Governments thundered **recriminations**, attorneys pleaded to the international Court of Justice at the Hague, the World Health Organization passed a special resolution, and even Great Britain's Prince Philip said he would "march down the Champs Elysées carrying a protest banner" if it would do any good. But France was determined to go ahead with plans for yet another nuclear test. This was to be the twenty-fourth and biggest of them all.

The testing site was to be Mururoa Atoll in the southern Pacific ocean, 750 miles southeast of Tahiti and 4,000 miles from Australia and South America. France believed that an "independent" nuclear force was vital to its defense, and contended that it had a right to carry out these tests because France alone among the nuclear powers had not perfected the trigger mechanism necessary to set off a hydrogen bomb. In terms of research, France was at a point reached by the United States twenty years earlier. Moreover, the United States had set off 188 in-air explosions to perfect its nuclear arsenal, and Russia had tested 142 times in the air, so why shouldn't France test for only the twenty-fourth time?

Two wrongs, or in this case three wrongs, do not make a right. The governments of Australia, New Zealand, and Peru (the countries most likely to suffer danger from the radioactive fallout) claimed that no one has a right to endanger the world's environment or pollute its atmosphere. The fact that the United States and Russia destroyed life in the past did not mean that the French had the right to do so again. There must never again be a repeat, they maintained, of what the United States did to the beautiful Pacific island of Bikini.

Before the spring of 1946, Bikini was exactly as you would imagine a South Pacific island. Soft waves lapped against its **coral** shores and an **azure** lagoon **teemed** with edible fish. A warm tropical breeze gently swayed the coconut palms, and cool springs provided fresh water. It was inhabited by 167 people whose families had been sheltered by the palms and had fished in the lagoon for many generations.

But all this changed in 1946 when the United States decided to use Bikini as the site for their atomic bomb tests. The islanders were told that the nuclear explosions were "for the good of mankind." They were shipped off at first to an island 130 miles away and then later to a larger island 210 miles away. Even though the islands were similar to Bikini, the move completely disrupted the lives of the people.

The Americans conducted twenty-three bomb tests on the island. These tests focused entirely on the use of atomic energy for war. The tests were carefully planned, but during the years of testing unexpected things happened. Radioactivity was often higher than expected, contaminating large areas. A shift in the wind following one **detonation** exposed 267 people to radiation. Several of these people suffered skin burns and loss of hair.

Finally, in 1958, the Americans deserted Bikini. For the next ten years scientists measured the radioactive fallout until finally, in August 1968, they pronounced the level of poisonous radiation low enough for the Bikinians to return "home."

The clear tropical waters of the lagoon awaited the islanders, but strange steel towers, ruined by the weather, stood in their waters. No tall coconut palms bade a graceful welcome; instead there was a growth of tangled brush that covered the entire island. Two nearby islands no longer existed, for they had been blown off the map during the testing. Coconut crabs and arrowroot were **taboo** foods, since their high level of **strontium** 90 would poison the eater.

Everything had changed. Only the island cemetery remained untouched. Houses, the school, and the church all had to be rebuilt. It would cost more than a million dollars to restore the island which had been taken for the "good of mankind," and years would pass before it would ever return to its former state.

Will it ever be truly the same? One wonders. Not only is there the possibility that the level of radiation may still be a danger (for even though scientists have verified it is safe, do they really know all the **repercussions** of nuclear testing?), but there is the problem of the people. How can life be the same for those 167 who were suddenly whisked away from their rightful inheritance for so many years? Their fate raises the fundamental issue; do we, or the French, or the Russians, or anyone else for that matter, have the right to decide alone what is "for the good of humanity"?

THINKING IT OVER

(1) What important events took place on Bikini? _____

_____

(2) What did the writer feel was the most unfortunate aspect of the Bikini affair? _____

_____

STUDYING THE PASSAGE

(1) Find the Main Idea: Choose one answer.
   (a) Bikini was used to test nuclear weapons.
   (b) An analysis of nuclear testing.
   (c) The pros and cons of nuclear testing.
   (d) The impact of nuclear testing on people.   _____

(2) Find the Facts: Mark each of these *true* or *false*.
   (a) The United States asked the Bikini islanders if they could use the island.   (a) _____
   (b) France's testing site was to be in the southern Pacific ocean.   (b) _____
   (c) Australia, Peru, and New Zealand agreed to the tests.   (c) _____
   (d) The Bikinians were away from their island for over two decades.   (d) _____
   (e) The tests were carefully planned.   (e) _____

(f) It was a decade after the tests before the radiation level was
    declared low enough for the Bikinians to return. (f) _____

(g) There was nothing left on the island. (g) _____

(h) The coconut crabs contained too high a level of strontium
    90 to be eaten. (h) _____

(3) Find the Order: Number the following in the order in which they appear in the passage.

(a) Bikini was inhabited by 167 people who had fished in the lagoon
    for many generations. (a) _____

(b) Will it ever be the same? (b) _____

(c) They shipped off the 167 inhabitants to other islands
    hundreds of miles away. (c) _____

(d) The fact that the United States and Russia had destroyed life in the
    past did not mean the French had the right to do it again. (d) _____

(e) The Americans finally deserted Bikini in 1958. (e) _____

(f) Two wrongs, or in this case three wrongs, do not make a right. (f) _____

(g) The World Health Organization passed a special resolution. (g) _____

(h) Several suffered skin burns and loss of hair. (h) _____

(4) Go beyond the Facts: Choose one. What does the writer imply by
    telling about Bikini?

(a) The Bikinians would never have given up their island if they had
    known how it would be devastated.

(b) The Bikinians will never again be able to grow food on the island.

(c) What was done to the Bikinians was not really "for the good
    of humanity."

(d) The Bikinians were not taken far enough away from the site to
    protect them from the poisonous radiation. _____

(5) Determine the Writer's Style and Technique: What is the tone of the passage?

(a) Pleading.

(b) Protesting.

(c) Nostalgic.

(d) Emotional. _____

(6) Words and Their Meanings: In the passage find the boldface word which fits each of these definitions.

_____   (a)   light purplish-blue in color

_____   (b)   indirect or far-off effects of some action

_____   (c)   counter-accusations

_____   (d)   a violent explosion

_____   (e)   a limestone substance formed from the skeletons of certain simple sea animals

_____   (f)   filled to overflowing; swarmed

_____   (g)   forbidden

_____   (h)   a radioactive substance created during nuclear explosion, dangerous to humans because of its similarity to calcium and its ability to be deposited in the human body in place of calcium

HOW TO OUTWIT YOUR OPPONENT

ABOUT THE PASSAGE   When you play a game with someone, you probably want to win. How you decide on the best way to do this may be influenced by some very innovative thinking that has taken place in mathematics and philosophy during the twentieth century.

REASON FOR READING   To follow the logical explanation for the use of one kind of strategy.

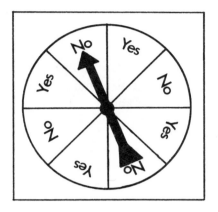

READ THE PASSAGE

Uncertainty in life has always been something humans have had to contend with. Each generation has developed its own systems for adjusting to uncertainty and making choices. Philosophers and mathematicians have been interested in ways to make accurate **inferences**, to make estimations, and to test **hypotheses** accurately. Of all possible courses of action, which is best, and which is next best? During the twentieth century several works were written about the nature of **strategy**. These were about the theory of games.

Game theory is a branch of mathematics that studies strategy, whether it is in business, selling new products, war, or in games of competition and sport. It should not be confused with **probability theory**, which applies to situations where all events happen (or fail to happen) according to luck or chance. Strategy is controlable by the players; luck is not. Game theory helps one adopt the best variations in play to avoid being beaten; it helps make the best of a bad situation and it helps avoid the worst of a good situation.

When you and your opponent are locked in combat, what is the best strategy to follow? No matter what your **scheme**, there is always the chance that your opponent will discover it and beat you. This is particularly so if the two of you are about evenly matched.

To prevent your opponent from **thwarting** you, game theory holds that there is only one possible way to be sure your adversary does not know your plan of action: do not know it yourself. In other words you **randomize** your strategy by using some device of chance, such as a drawing by lot or a "spinner." You create an unpredictable pattern for mixing your plays. For example, if you wanted to **bluff** 10 percent of the time, you could write *bluff* on one slip of paper and *don't bluff* on nine slips of paper. Then you would draw the slips of paper from a hat. Since you yourself do not know in advance whether you are going to bluff, how can your opponent possibly out-guess you?

Strategies may be either pure (simple) or mixed (randomized). A pure or simple strategy is an advance list of instructions telling you exactly what to do in every possible circumstance according to the moves your opponent makes. Tick-Tack-Toe is a game where pure strategy can be used. Complete information regarding the outcome is available on every possible move, both by you and by your opponent. Thus, if the players are evenly matched, the game will always end in a tie; one can lose only by making a mistake.

But more often complete information is not possible and so on-the-spot decisions have to be made. This is when randomized or mixed strategy can be used beneficially.

THINKING IT OVER

(1) What is the difference between game theory and probability theory? _____

_____

_____

(2) According to the passage, what is the benefit of using a randomized strategy? _____

_____

STUDYING THE PASSAGE

(1) Find the Main Idea: Choose one answer.
   (a) Game theory should not be confused with probability theory.
   (b) Game theory explains how to use strategy.
   (c) Theory of games is an ancient way of dealing with uncertainty.
   (d) Strategies are of two kinds.   _____

(2) Find the Facts: Mark each of these *true* or *false*.
   (a) Probability relies on strategy.   (a) _____
   (b) Mathematicians and philosophers have been interested
        in uncertainty.   (b) _____
   (c) Game theory helps a player adopt the best variations in play to avoid
        being beaten.   (c) _____
   (d) You must keep to a consistent pattern of plays in order to win. (d) _____
   (e) One way to randomize a strategy is to use some device of chance,
        such as a spinner.   (e) _____
   (f) Strategies are usually pure.   (f) _____
   (g) A pure strategy is an advance list of instructions covering all
        possible moves.   (g) _____
   (h) In a mixed strategy, complete information is available on every
        possible move.   (h) _____

(3) Find the Order: Number the following in the order in which they appear in the passage.

(a) There is always a chance that your opponent will discover your strategy.   (a) _____

(b) Game theory helps make the best of a bad situation.   (b) _____

(c) Strategy is controllable by players; luck is not.   (c) _____

(d) Game theory is used in business and war.   (d) _____

(e) One can only lose a game of pure strategy if one makes a mistake.   (e) _____

(f) Tick-Tack-Toe is a game where pure strategy can be used.   (f) _____

(g) A spinner can be used to make an unpredictable pattern for mixing your moves.   (g) _____

(h) To keep from being beaten, the best strategy is not to know your own strategy.   (h) _____

(4) Go beyond the Facts: Which two statements seem the most logical extensions of the passage?

(a) You could use game theory in chess or bridge, but not in dice or roulette.

(b) Game theory is not applicable to business or politics.

(c) Game theory is a mathematical model of real life situations.

(d) Game theory does not apply to games which involve more than two players.   _____ _____

(5) Determine the Writer's Style and Technique: Which one of the following best describes the way the writer presents the facts?

(a) Uses facts to explain an idea.

(b) Makes an analogy to show what something is.

(c) Tells a story to illustrate a fact.

(d) Uses comparison and contrast to define something.   _____

(6) Words and Their Meanings: In the passage find the boldface word which fits each of these definitions.

_____ (a) to fool another person by a false show of strength

_____ (b) conclusions derived from facts or premises

_____ (c) theories or assumptions made in order to test the consequences of their truth

_____ (d) a branch of math which studies the likelihood of the occurrence of an event

_____ (e) to arrange without any definite order

_____ (f) a plan of action, sometimes unethical

_____ (g) overall planning designed to gain some objective or to defeat an opponent

_____ (h) blocking, frustrating, defeating

STARS*

ABOUT THE PASSAGE

If you travel by car or bike across the United States, you begin to sense how vast this country is, and by comparison, how large the earth is too. But when compared with other planets in this solar system, the earth is small. Often the sense of size, when considering the universe, becomes almost unimaginable. In this passage you will be asked to think about the enormous dimensions of some stars and the tiny size of the atoms that compose them.

REASON FOR READING

To read a factual, technical account and then to try to sort out facts to answer specific questions.

READ THE PASSAGE

Stars, which we all have seen at night, are self-**luminous** objects. They give off heat and light which come from within themselves. Unlike the planets, they do not reflect light. In the universe there are billions of stars, few of them identical or even similar. Of all these stars only about 6000 are visible to the unaided eye.

The biggest known star is called Epsilon Aurigae B. It is almost 2 billion miles in **diameter**—2,000 times the diameter of the sun. Epsilon Aurigae B is so big that the sun and the earth, with the 93 million miles between them, could be placed almost 20 times across the middle of this giant star.

Astronomers believe there is a limit to how large a star can become. Even the biggest ordinary stars are only about 100 times the **mass** of the sun, which is 330,000 times the mass of the earth. A star more massive than this, they think, either explodes or begins to shrink.

Stars, like living things, have life **spans** and change as they get older. Scientists think stars are born when tiny particles of dust in space swirl together in a big, cloudlike ball. As more and more dust collects, the **gravity** becomes stronger and the dust cloud contracts, becoming smaller. The cloud particles build up pressure as they squash together. The pressure makes the dust cloud hotter and hotter until it begins to glow as a star. For a time, the star gives off heat and light as it burns its fuel.

Then, as the star continues to burn, it shrinks until, after billions of years, it becomes as small as a planet. It is then white hot and is called a white dwarf. The atoms in a white dwarf are packed tightly together, making it enormously **dense**. At this point, no more contraction can take place; the star has no more fuel to burn. As it cools, the white dwarf changes from white to red to a final black. A cold dark cinder, the star, now dead, becomes part of the interstellar **debris** from which future stars can be made.

Some stars that begin with a greater mass than the sun develop and die in a different way. But to understand what happens to them it is important to review the basic structure of all matter.

Everything is made up of atoms—particles so tiny that there are billions and billions of them in a drop of water. But each atom is like a miniature solar system. The nucleus, or center, is like the sun. Whirling around the nucleus at fantastic speeds are the electrons, almost weightless electrical charges.

*Part of the information has been adapted, by permission of Random House, Inc., from *What's the Biggest?* by Barbara Fogel. © Copyright 1966 by Barbara R. Fogel.

Tiny as the atom is, it is mostly space. If you could take the space out of your body and squash together the nuclei and electrons in the atoms, you would be as small as a grain of sand. But that "grain" would weigh just as much as you do now.

In stars of mass greater than the sun, gravitational pull forces the star to fall in upon itself. This creates tremendous pressure and heat. This pressure is so great it drives the electrons of all the atoms composing the star right into the atomic nuclei. When this happens the heat and pressure are too much—the star explodes and creates for a time a glow that is brighter than that of an entire galaxy. This explosion is called a *supernova*. Hot gases will remain visible for thousands of years until eventually they vanish as they are spread through space.

The only thing remaining will be a tiny ball of neutrons, not much larger than 10 miles in diameter, created by the force of the explosion. But the density of this tiny ball is so great that a fragment the size of a bouillon cube would weigh a billion tons. This object is called a neutron star.

In the 1960s astronomers only theorized about the existence of such substances, but by the 1970s they had detected their presence. Through the work of a young Irish woman, Jocelyn Bell, and other astronomers at Cambridge University in England, a regular **pulsating** radio signal detected by a special telescope proved after careful and thorough examination to be a neutron star.

THINKING IT OVER

(1) Compare the diameter of the biggest known star to that of the sun. _____

_____

(2) What is a white dwarf and what are its characteristics? _____

_____

_____

(3) Neutron stars are not known for their great size. What is their exceptional characteristic?_____

_____

STUDYING THE PASSAGE
(1) Find the Main Idea: Choose one answer.
   (a) Compare stars with planets.
   (b) Explain the infinity of the universe.
   (c) Describe the nature and composition of stars.
   (d) Summarize the history of astronomy.   _____

(2) Find the Facts: Mark each of these *true* or *false*.

    (a)   The biggest known star is called Epsilon Aurigae B.   (a) _____

    (b)   Epsilon Aurigae B is so big it is twenty times larger than the sun and earth and the space between them.   (b) _____

    (c)   Stars die.   (c) _____

    (d)   Scientists think that stars were originally clouds of dust swirling in space.   (d) _____

    (e)   The pull of gravity causes the dust clouds to expand so the star becomes larger.   (e) _____

    (f)   Tiny as the atom is, it is mostly space.   (f) _____

    (g)   If you took all the space out of your body, you would still weigh the same.   (g) _____

    (h)   Neutron stars are bigger than any other kind of stars.   (h) _____

(3) Find the Order: Number the following in the order in which they appear in the passage.

    (a)   Jocelyn Bell detected a neutron star.   (a) _____

    (b)   As the star burns up its fuel, it shrinks.   (b) _____

    (c)   The white dwarf changes from white to red to a final black.   (c) _____

    (d)   Astronomers think even the biggest ordinary stars are only about 100 times the mass of the sun.   (d) _____

    (e)   Each atom is like a miniature solar system.   (e) _____

    (f)   Stars have life spans and change as they get older.   (f) _____

    (g)   The cloud particles build up pressure as they squash together.   (g) _____

    (h)   A star is born when tiny particles of dust gather into a ball.   (h) _____

(4) Go beyond the Facts: Which one would not be a conclusion you might reach from reading this passage?

    (a)   Human beings are pretty insignificant when seen in relation to the rest of the universe.

    (b)   Nothing in the universe remains the same.

    (c)   The greater part of the universe is made up of space.

    (d)   Human beings and the other things in the universe are basically made up of quite different materials.   _____

(5) Determine the Writer's Style and Technique: To which would you say this style of writing is best suited? Choose one.

    (a)   A journal for astronomers.

    (b)   A science textbook.

    (c)   A magazine.

    (d)   An editorial.   _____

(6) Words and Their Meanings: In the passage find the boldface word which fits each of these definitions.

_____   (a)   force of attraction between one piece of matter and another; pull

_____   (b)   lengths of time

_____   (c)   scattered remains of something broken; ruins

_____   (d)   a straight line passing through the center of a circle or sphere from one edge to the other

_____   (e)   crowded, compact

_____   (f)   expanding and contracting rhythmically

_____   (g)   the property of a body that is taken as a measure of the amount of material it contains and causes it to have weight

_____   (h)   giving off light

THE DIVING WOMEN OF KOREA AND JAPAN

ABOUT THE PASSAGE

Along the island coastlines of Korea and Japan live some 30,000 women divers known as *ama*. Their outstanding physical ability to make strenuous dives continuously in cold waters comes, scientists believe, from persistent and careful training begun at an early age. Proud of their 1500-year-old profession, these women continue to gather food for their families and communities.

REASON FOR READING

To learn about ways the human body adapts to some unaccustomed stresses.

READ THE PASSAGE

Loud, short whistles are heard at a long distance on the small, rocky island. Farmers in the midst of their work lift their heads. The whistle is a sign to all who hear it that the divers known as the *ama* are preparing to dive. On this island, Cheju, just south of Korea, live almost 11,000 women who make their living by diving. Their quest is rich shellfish and edible seaweeds that thrive in the coastal waters of Cheju. Almost all of the divers are women.

The women are famous throughout the world for their breath-holding dives which frequently take them to depths of 80 feet. Even though the water is often only 50°F. in the winter, many of the Korean divers work year round.

Diving is a lifelong profession, and many begin working in the shallow waters when they are girls of eleven or twelve and may continue the work until they are sixty-five years old. A pregnant ama will often dive up to the day of delivery of her baby and continue working shortly after, caring for the infant during rest periods. The ama usually work three long shifts in summer and two short shifts in winter. They wear **minimal** clothing, a loincloth, and in winter a cotton bathing suit. Their only equipment is a glass face mask or goggles. When introduced almost a century ago, the goggles harmed the eyes when used at depths of greater than 10 feet because of unequal water pressure. The ama added a small air-filled bag to regulate air pressure behind the lenses. Today they are able to equalize the water pressure on the face masks by their own breathing.

Two kinds of dives are practiced: one is from a boat with an assistant; the other is alone from a float. In the first kind of dive, the woman attaches a counter weight to her (about 30 pounds) that pulls her to the bottom rapidly; she gathers the food and then is pulled to the surface by her helper in the boat. In the second kind the diver dives from the float, gathers food, then surfaces at the float, which is equipped with a net to hold her catch.

In the assisted dive a diver takes fifteen seconds to descend, uses thirty seconds to gather, and is pulled back to the surface in fifteen seconds. She rests a minute, gets her breath, and then dives again, averaging thirty dives an hour. The advantages of this type of dive are a longer time searching for food and the chance to search deeper, less **accessible** waters.

The unassisted diver takes five seconds to descend, searches for fifteen seconds, and surfaces in another five seconds. For thirty seconds she rests and breathes and then dives again. She averages sixty dives an hour, twice as many as the assisted diver, but has less time at the bottom and is limited to shallower waters that are more thoroughly and frequently searched. The diving women do not experience the bends, a serious, sometimes fatal reaction of divers caused by the **accumulation** of too much nitrogen in the blood while below the surface and losing it too quickly while returning to the surface. The women know from long experience the limits of safety for them. They do quick, shallow dives that they can repeat again and again.

Physiologists have studied the ama to determine what changes might be occurring in the divers that enable them to do daily work that places such stress on the body's lung capacity and ability to retain heat. The ama are different from nondivers in several ways. First, they have a great capacity for taking in large amounts of oxygen in a single breath and can hold it up to two minutes. The ama **hyperventilate** before each dive, and it is at this time that they emit the characteristic whistle as they expel their breath. Their great oxygen-holding capacity does not seem to be a hereditary trait. The women acquire their capabilities by training. The training, however, is essential.

Their heartbeat, which speeds up rapidly as they hyperventilate before they dive, drops greatly during their dive, then rises to normal when they return to the surface. Although scientists do not know exactly why the heart beat slows during the dive, they do know that the slowed heartbeat enables a diver to stay under water longer because the body uses less of the oxygen taken during the rapid breathing.

Another factor that affects the length of the amas' dive is the slow rate at which their bodies lose heat. The women had a body temperature close to 95°F. after a diving shift usually forty minutes in summer and twenty-five minutes in winter. The ama tend to eat 3000 calories daily, while a nondiving woman eats about 1000 less. The extra food of the ama goes toward counterbalancing the extreme stress of the cold, for the diving women are not heavy; on the contrary, they are unusually lean.

The ama possess two defenses against the cold of their daily environment. One is a higher **metabolic rate**. They burn calories faster, giving the body more heat internally. But, in addition, their bodies' ability to retain heat is very great. The layer of fat just under the skin is the most important factor in retaining body heat. This fat does not conduct heat rapidly and therefore forms a good insulator (keeping heat in and cold out). It is well known that whales and seals are able to live in arctic and antarctic waters because they have thick layers of fat. It is well known, too, that in a woman's body the proportion of fat to muscle is greater than in a man's. Women are far better insulated against cold than men, and it is likely that this is the reason women dominate in the Korean and Japanese diving profession.

In one test conducted on the ama to determine the insulation of the ama's body from the cold, participants in the test reclined for three hours in water at 83°F. The ama did not shiver during the test. Non-diving women began shivering at 86°F. and male nondivers shivered at 88°F. The scientists concluded that the lack of shivering in the ama was a result of their training, a kind of hardening. This lack of shivering is indeed a help, for through shivering they would speed up the loss of heat through the skin.

The amas' occupation is at least 1,500 years old. The evidence of archaeologists suggests that people were diving before the fourth century on Cheju, where the profession is believed to have originated. But as the twentieth century closes, fewer women are taking up this demanding and skilled profession since other jobs, more **lucrative** and less **arduous**, are available. For those ama who have continued, there is a strong resistance to the use of modern diving equipment, such as scuba gear. Even though this would make it possible to complete the same amount of work more easily in a shorter time using fewer people, these results would be harmful to the women's communities. Hundreds of women who feed their families in this way would be out of work, and the sea bottoms and coastal waters would be harvested too quickly. Many villages in Japan have even outlawed the foam-rubber suit for diving.

THINKING IT OVER

(1) Why are the women able to make such remarkable dives? _____

_____

(2) What details suggest that the ama are sensible about their work? _____

_____

(3) In what four ways have the bodies of the ama adapted so that they can make repeated deep dives?

_____

STUDYING THE PASSAGE

(1) Find the Main Idea: Choose one answer.
   (a) The ama are famous divers.
   (b) The ama provide an example of how the human body adapts to different stresses.
   (c) Resisting modern conveniences may not be wise.
   (d) Diving is a wonderful sport.   _____

(2) Find the Facts: Mark each of these *true* or *false*.
   (a) The women divers were born with exceptional diving abilities.   (a) _____
   (b) The ama usually stop diving when they marry.   (b) _____
   (c) The ama make dives to 80 feet.   (c) _____
   (d) The ama wouldn't be able to make their dives without their special
        diving gear.   (d) _____
   (e) Women make better divers than men because of their proportion of
        fat just below the skin.   (e) _____
   (f) The women hyperventilate before each dive to obtain a large store
        of oxygen.   (f) _____
   (g) Because their work is so strenuous and time-consuming, the ama
        do not have children.   (g) _____
   (h) Though the ama have only been diving for about a century, they have
        developed great skill at it.   (h) _____

(3) Find the Order: Number the following in the order in which they appear in the passage.
   (a) The extra food of the ama goes toward balancing the extreme
        stress of the cold.   (a) _____
   (b) Diving is a lifelong profession.   (b) _____
   (c) The women do not experience the bends.   (c) _____
   (d) The women acquire their great capabilities by training.   (d) _____
   (e) The whistle is a sign to all that the ama are preparing to dive.   (e) _____
   (f) There is a strong resistance to the use of modern diving equipment.   (f) _____
   (g) Two kinds of dives are practiced: the assisted and the unassisted.   (g) _____

(4) Go beyond the Facts: Choose one. From this passage one can conclude that the ama do not want to use modern diving equipment because:
   (a) They do not want to upset the present balance that exists between the rate at which they gather food and the rate at which the ocean creates that food.
   (b) They are afraid of new inventions.
   (c) They don't respect anything that is too easy to do.
   (d) It is too heavy.   _____

(5) Determine the Writer's Style and Technique: Which one method best describes the way the information is given in this passage?
   (a) Factual account.
   (b) Legend.
   (c) Opinion.
   (d) Dramatization.   _____

(6) Words and Their Meanings: In the passage find the boldface word which fits each of these definitions.

   _____   (a) scientists who study the function, activities, and processes of the living body

   _____   (b) the smallest amount necessary to be adequate or enough

   _____   (c) demanding energy and stamina

   _____   (d) makes a lot of money

   _____   (e) that which has built up or collected gradually

   _____   (f) available; able to be reached

   _____   (g) breathing very deeply and rapidly

   _____   (h) rate at which food is converted into energy and made available to the body and its processes

DIAMONDS

ABOUT THE PASSAGE | Referred to as "the stuff dreams are made of," diamonds are known also as the hardest substance on earth. Dug from the earth, mined by thousands of people on one continent, diamonds are controlled and sold around the world by people in just one company.

REASON FOR READING | To learn the uses, characteristics, and historical details of an unusual substance.

READ THE PASSAGE

What do a phonograph needle, a dentist's drill, and an oil-drilling rig have in common? Nothing, you say? Yet common to all three is the hardest substance known—the diamond. The word itself comes from the ancient Greek word *adamas*, not breakable. Even the Greeks, living several centuries before Christ, had heard of the fiery, brilliant, hard stone known as the diamond.

The atoms found in diamonds are the same as those found in charcoal; they are also the same as the atoms in graphite, the material of which pencils are made. The only chemical difference between these three minerals is the arrangement of the carbon atoms they all contain. The more **symmetrical** the arrangement of the carbon atoms, the closer to a diamond the substance becomes. The atoms of carbon in charcoal are arranged in no particular order; those of graphite are arranged in sheets like bathroom tile, which make it move smoothly over paper. But the atoms in a diamond are arranged in a very symmetrical order, formed in the earth under great temperature and pressure. This process results in a stone which is extremely hard and **transparent**. It is because of the special conditions required for diamonds to be formed that they are relatively rare.

There are two uses of diamonds: gem and industrial. Gem diamonds are made into jewels. When diamonds first come from the earth, they are dull, almost greasy in appearance. They must be cleaned and cut to reveal the fire and brilliance that is the characteristic of this gem. The finest diamonds are pure carbon and colorless; they are perfectly clear and transparent. Blue, pink, green, and yellow diamonds are highly prized if the coloring is distinct and uniform. The standard measurement of gem diamonds is the metric carat. This is equal to .200 grams or 200 milligrams. Because diamonds are so hard, cutting them into **facets** is an extremely skilled and specialized job.

Although most people recognize and value the diamond as a gem or jewel, it is as a tool that the diamond most directly affects our daily living. Industrial diamonds are so important that a shortage would cause a breakdown in the modern metalworking industry and would **devastate** mass production. Industrial diamonds are crushed and powdered and these powders are used in many grinding and polishing operations. They are used, for example, in grinding wheels for the sharpening of cutting tools. Sometimes they are **suspended** in water. Their use ranges from the drill in a dentist's office to saws for cutting rocks, to glass cutters. The great hardness of a diamond makes it one of the finest **abrasive** materials known.

People have long wanted to make imitation diamonds because of the **arduous** tasks involved in mining natural diamonds and because of the great value of this gem. Though two men in the early twentieth century claimed they had **synthesized** a diamond, no one could repeat their work, and so it wasn't until 1955 that diamond synthesis was successful. General Electric did this by subjecting carbon substances to pressures in excess of 1,500,000 lbs/in² (pounds per square inch) and a temperature above 5000°F. At that time General Electric sold its diamonds at the same price that natural diamonds were sold. In 1959 they made public their method of manufacture.

Diamonds have been known since very early times and the oldest come from India. During the eighteenth century South America was a primary source; during the twentieth century Africa has become the major supplier of diamonds for the world. This very profitable business of mining and selling diamonds is in the hands of just one company and its **subsidiaries,** the DeBeers Consolidated Mines Limited. This company, formed in the early twentieth century by Cecil Rhodes, a British citizen, operates in South Africa. Most of the work is done by Africans who may benefit very little from the huge profits the company makes from its sale and control of diamonds.

THINKING IT OVER

(1) Which one of the following does not belong with the others?
    (a) Charcoal.
    (b) Graphite.
    (c) Glass.
    (d) Diamond. _____

(2) Explain your answer to question 1. _____
_____

(3) What makes the other three members of the group different from one another? _____
_____

STUDYING THE PASSAGE

(1) Find the Main Idea: Choose one answer.
    (a) Diamonds are necessary in our technical world.
    (b) Diamonds are expensive and hard to find.
    (c) Diamonds are valued for both their beauty and their usefulness.
    (d) How diamonds can be duplicated. _____

(2) Find the Facts: Mark each of these *true* or *false*.
    (a) A diamond is formed under great temperature and pressure.   (a) _____
    (b) Charcoal is made of highly organized atoms.   (b) _____
    (c) The more symmetrical the arrangement of the atoms, the closer to a diamond the carbon becomes.   (c) _____
    (d) Diamonds come in only one color.   (d) _____
    (e) It was only in the 1970s that humans have been able to develop a good substitute for a real diamond.   (e) _____
    (f) Most diamonds are now mined in Alaska.   (f) _____
    (g) Synthetic diamonds have cost as much as natural ones.   (g) _____
    (h) The people who mine the diamonds are very rich.   (h) _____

(3) Find the Order: Number the following in the order in which they appear in the passage.

    (a) Those in graphite are arranged in sheets like bathroom tile.   (a) _____

    (b) General Electric made a synthetic diamond.   (b) _____

    (c) At first diamonds are dull, almost greasy-looking.   (c) _____

    (d) They are the same as the atoms in graphite.   (d) _____

    (e) A diamond is one of the finest abrasives known.   (e) _____

    (f) Many Africans who mine the diamonds do not benefit from their sale.   (f) _____

    (g) A diamond cutter is a very skilled worker.   (g) _____

    (h) Diamond comes from the ancient Greek word for "not breakable."   (h) _____

(4) Go beyond the Facts: This writer implies which one of the following?

    (a) Technological progress is not possible without diamonds.

    (b) People prefer imitation diamonds because they are even better than those produced by nature.

    (c) People are deceived in thinking diamonds are something special.

    (d) Diamonds—whether natural or synthetic—are highly valued because they are so difficult to obtain.   _____

(5) Determine the Writer's Style and Technique: Decide which method the writer uses.

    (a) Facts and description.

    (b) Symbolism.

    (c) Cause and effect.

    (d) Logical sequence.   _____

(6) Words and Their Meanings: In the passage find the boldface word which fits each of these definitions.

_____ (a) harsh, rough; of or pertaining to being used for grinding and polishing

_____ (b) hung so as to be free on all sides

_____ (c) strenuous; very difficult

_____ (d) to bring to complete ruin or disorder

_____ (e) small plane surfaces; faces

_____ (f) produced by combining chemicals or compounds; not produced naturally

_____ (g) balanced; precisely matching on each side

_____ (h) capable of being seen through

_____ (i) a company controlled by another company

Selection 15 — Subject: Science
Theme: The World of Animals, Insects, and Reptiles

BORROWING FROM NATURE

ABOUT THE PASSAGE   By watching other animals, human beings have learned things that
                       have contributed to several twentieth-century inventions.

REASON FOR READING   To observe how a writer develops an idea by using examples.

READ THE PASSAGE

A bee stings you on your big toe. A squid shoots through the ocean to avoid a **predator**. A porpoise uses sonar to locate its position and its food. Moths, butterflies, birds, and many other animals are colored so that they blend perfectly with their environment to reduce their chances of being caught. Many moths can send "radar" waves to scramble the waves being sent by the bats that eat them. The whale, even though it can weigh tons, moves through the water with speed and grace.

These are all examples of natural occurrences that humans have copied. A **hypodermic** needle, through which we receive life-saving drugs, works much like a bee's stinger. Both pump fluid into the bloodstream.

The squid uses a jet of ocean water to shoot itself through the deep; a jet motorboat also uses a stream of **compressed** water to produce its movement. Both the squid and the boat can control the force of the water jet to **regulate** their speeds.

A porpoise sends out sound waves. These waves move through the water and bounce off the objects they encounter. The **reflected** waves then move back through the water and are perceived by the porpoise, which adjusts its direction according to the incoming messages. Our scientists use sonar frequently to locate the posi-

tion of underwater objects or to map the geography of the ocean floor, and radar can detect objects that are approaching by air. Both of these systems work on an echo principle— bouncing waves off solid objects and receiving the return signal.

Bats, too, use echolocation, sending out ultrahigh frequency sound waves to detect **luscious** moths or other insects. The moth, however, can send out its own **ultrasonic** signals. The moth and bat wave patterns become mixed, and the message to the bat is so scrambled that it cannot locate the moth's position. In the same manner, if a modern warplane detects radar from enemy sources, it can send out signals that scramble the enemy radar.

For a long time, hunters and soldiers have **camouflaged** themselves with clothing or paint or some other materials. In so doing, they are using another principle illustrated by nature: if an organism blends with its environment, it has a greater probability of survival.

We have used whales to help us design large submarines, copying those beautifully streamlined bodies which move so rapidly through the water. During this century a branch of science called *bionics* has devoted itself to investigating and adapting plant and animal mechanisms for use in human inventions.

THINKING IT OVER

(1) How does a bat locate its prey, and in what way is this principle useful to humans? _____

_____

(2) Which of the following is probably a way that humans have copied the spider web?
   (a)   An army tank.
   (b)   A fishing net.
   (c)   A sewing thread.
   (d)   A trampoline.   _____

STUDYING THE PASSAGE

(1) Find the Main Idea: Choose one answer.
   (a)   Porpoises use sonar to locate food.
   (b)   There are many similarities between animals and the inventions
          of human beings.
   (c)   Motorboats work much like a squid.
   (d)   Humans borrow ideas from things in nature.   _____

(2) Find the Facts: Mark each of these *true* or *false*.
   (a)   Many moths can send out ultrasonic signals.   (a) _____
   (b)   Hypodermic needles work like rhinoceros horns.   (b) _____
   (c)   The squid can control its jet of water.   (c) _____
   (d)   A bee sends out radar.   (d) _____
   (e)   Soldiers learned about camouflage by observing bats.   (e) _____
   (f)   Warplanes can send out scrambling radar.   (f) _____
   (g)   Sonar can be used to map ocean floors.   (g) _____
   (h)   Radar and sonar work on an echo principle.   (h) _____

(3) Find the Order: Number the following in the order in which they appear in the passage.
   (a)   A squid moves with a jet of water.   (a) _____
   (b)   The message to the bat gets scrambled.   (b) _____
   (c)   Some whales weigh tons.   (c) _____
   (d)   If an organism blends with its environment there is greater
          chance for survival.   (d) _____
   (e)   Scientists use sonar.   (e) _____
   (f)   A bee and a hypodermic needle pump fluid into our bloodstream.   (f) _____
   (g)   Porpoise sound waves are reflected off underwater objects.   (g) _____
   (h)   A bee stings you on your big toe.   (h) _____

(4) Go beyond the Facts: Which one of the following is the best conclusion
     to be reached from the information in this passage?
   (a)   Many of our "inventions" are simply copies from nature.
   (b)   Human beings could not invent things without having examples
          from nature to copy.
   (c)   Wild creatures are more inventive than men.
   (d)   All our inventions are copied from nature.   _____

53

(5) Determine the Writer's Style and Technique: Choose one.
   Which method does the writer use?
   (a) Uses an analogy.
   (b) Tells a story.
   (c) Uses arguments.
   (d) States facts.   _____

(6) Words and Their Meanings: In the passage find the boldface word which fits
   each of these definitions.

   _____   (a) bounced off something

   _____   (b) disguised or masked so as to resemble one's surroundings
                                    and thus prevent detection

   _____   (c) reduced in size or volume by pressure

   _____   (d) an organism that preys on others

   _____   (e) to control

   _____   (f) of very high frequency, not audible to the human ear

   _____   (g) delicious

   _____   (h) relating to the parts beneath the skin

LAND RECLAMATION

ABOUT THE PASSAGE

Slowly, persistently, and for a long time, people have filled in bays, estuaries, and marshes. Their purpose—to create usable land from seemingly wasted, unproductive areas. Recently some people are suggesting that these supposedly useless watery areas are essential to human life.

REASON FOR READING

To notice how the writer organizes her facts to support a certain opinion.

READ THE PASSAGE

In many countries that border on water, there has been **extensive** land **reclamation**. Bays, **estuaries**, marshes, and wetlands are all affected. Land can be reclaimed by filling in the water-covered areas with rock and soil taken from higher ground. Seventeenth-century Boston, for example, **originally** consisted of 470 acres. By the last quarter of the twentieth century there were 3,240 acres of city real estate. Back Bay, one section of the city that borders the Charles River, was once 400 acres of marsh that was filled with dirt and rock from nearby Beacon Hill.

In the San Francisco Bay area, the original 700 square miles of bay has shrunk to 435 square miles because it has been filled with earth from other sections. Foster City is completely built on the reclaimed lands of San Francisco Bay. In time, the bay may become no larger than a drainage ditch.

Land can also be reclaimed by building dams and draining water out of the area. In the Netherlands, dikes or dams have been built to close off the Ijsselmeer (formerly known as the Zuider Zee), a large shallow bay formed by the North Sea. The Dutch are draining the water out of the enclosed area and using the "reclaimed" land, which was once part of the ocean floor, for farming and building homes. Areas of land reclaimed from the sea are known as polders.

This land reclamation is a good way for a large coastal city to expand its boundaries and its economy or for a **populous** country to add to its

agricultural lands. But many scientists are disturbed over this extensive loss of wetlands. Much reclamation takes place in the shallow, marshy flats and estuaries formed where river valleys meet the sea. These areas where tides invade the river and salt water mixes with fresh form one of the most productive environments on earth.

A great number of plant and animal forms, some **submicroscopic**, depend on estuaries as a nursery, a shelter, or a permanent home. Algae, cord grass, and eelgrass all **thrive**. Among their roots and stems crawl, curl, and swim great numbers of worms, protozoans, shrimp, clams, snails, oysters, salmon, and bass. Above these plants and animals fly the birds—swallows, gulls, egrets—that depend on them for food.

But in addition to the rich abundance of life that estuaries and other wetlands support directly, they provide other benefits to human life. As large bodies of water, they absorb great amounts of heat, helping to create a more pleasant climate. A **comparable** area of land would raise the temperature in the immediate vicinity considerably. These watery border zones between land and sea also provide open space, described by biologist Rene Dubos as a "biological necessity" of human beings. Then, too, their sandbars and large areas of shallow water break the fury of storms.

By filling in the estuaries, we remove the homes and shelters of many creatures; in destroying them, we **disrupt** natural processes which could affect human life. The teeming lives of estuaries, though stubborn, are fragile. Sewage clogs them, chemicals pollute them, and land fill smothers them.

There seems to be no clear-cut solution to this problem. One answer may lie in legislation. Laws might ensure the preservation and protection of the marshes, estuaries, wetlands, and bays. Any proposals for land reclamation which fills in wetlands should be carefully and thoroughly considered.

THINKING IT OVER

(1) Land reclamation is harmful for all of the following reasons except:
   (a) Fish cannot breed as well.
   (b) Local temperatures may increase.
   (c) Sewage is blocked up.
   (d) Houses and farms can be built on reclaimed land. _____

STUDYING THE PASSAGE

(1) Find the Main Idea: Choose one answer.
   (a) Fish are killed by land reclamation.
   (b) The key to proper land reclamation lies in legislation.
   (c) Land reclamation can be harmful if it is not adequately controlled.
   (d) Land reclamation occurs in two ways. _____

(2) Find the Facts: Mark each of these *true* or *false*.
   (a) Land can be reclaimed by dumping earth into the water.   (a) _____
   (b) Land can be reclaimed by draining water out of a bay.   (b) _____
   (c) The Dutch are filling in the Ijsselmeer with earth.   (c) _____
   (d) Foster City is built on reclaimed land.   (d) _____
   (e) Estuaries and other wetlands are not essential to human life.   (e) _____
   (f) Laws are the only way to solve the problem.   (f) _____
   (g) Reclaimed land has been important to Boston's growth.   (g) _____
   (h) Moderate weather is a benefit of living near wetlands.   (h) _____

(3) Find the Order: Number the following in the order in which they appear in the passage.
   (a) Scientists are disturbed by land reclamation.   (a) _____
   (b) Many countries are reclaiming land.   (b) _____
   (c) Shellfish live in estuaries.   (c) _____
   (d) The border zones provide open space.   (d) _____
   (e) Legislation is needed to protect wetlands.   (e) _____
   (f) The Dutch have built dams called dikes.   (f) _____
   (g) These waters break the fury of storms.   (g) _____
   (h) San Francisco Bay used to be 700 square miles.   (h) _____

(4) Go beyond the Facts: If sewage collects in a bay, which one of the following will probably show a decline in population?
   (a) Codfish.
   (b) Whales.
   (c) Shellfish.
   (d) Bass. _____

(5) Determine the Writer's Style and Technique: Which of the following best describes the way the writer presents her facts?

    (a) Compares and contrasts.

    (b) Arranges them in an argument.

    (c) Tells a story.

    (d) Uses an analogy.   _____

(6) Words and Their Meanings: In the passage find the boldface word which fits each of these definitions.

_____   (a) equivalent; similar

_____   (b) vast; widespread

_____   (c) first; pertaining to the earliest or beginning stage of something

_____   (d) interrupt; upset

_____   (e) the act of recovering or restoring

_____   (f) very small; too small to be seen by a microscope

_____   (g) to grow vigorously; flourish

_____   (h) places where fresh water from rivers mixes with salt water from ocean tides

_____   (i) crowded; thickly populated

HEAT FROM THE SUN

ABOUT THE PASSAGE

Finding sources other than fossil fuels for energy has become a major concern of industrialized nations in the last quarter of the twentieth century. The use of the sun as a source of energy has been known for thousands of years, but is now actively being explored.

REASON FOR READING

To learn how solar energy can be used to heat buildings.

READ THE PASSAGE

Now that the shortage of fossil fuels and their **impending** depletion is clear, the search is on for other fuels to keep homes and industries warm and working. One possibility is energy from the sun. During the late 1970s people began to show more interest in using the sun to heat homes and water and to **generate** electricity. The sun **radiates** a huge amount of heat, and some part of the earth is continuously touched by the sun. According to one scientist, the amount of sun falling on 2 percent of the land area of the United States could produce all the energy this country would need. The difficult challenge is to find ways of making this energy useable.

Many different ways of using the sun's heat have been developed. Usually solar energy systems are called active or **passive** depending on what equipment is used to absorb the sun's heat. Basically, passive systems involve allowing the sun's rays to enter a building to heat a material which will reradiate the heat after the sun has set. It uses no collectors or fans. In some large public buildings **fiberglass** wall panels allow sunlight to pass through to be absorbed by ceiling-high metal tubes filled with water. This hot water heats the air and provides the hot water in the building. Bead walls are a special construction that can be opened to gain heat and are closed to exclude or retain it. These have been used in an Aspen, Colorado air terminal.

Active solar energy systems make use of collectors. Active systems include some way of collecting the sun's heat in a heat collection medium such as water or antifreeze, and a heat storage material such as a rockbed or water. Fans or water pumps can then be used to distribute this warmth from the collecting site to other parts of the building. Solar collectors are usually mounted on the roof.

With both passive and active systems, but especially with passive systems, all details about the building are carefully considered. The angle at which a building is located is important; usually it faces south. Skylights and greenhouses are carefully placed. Using materials that transfer heat well and retain it is also important for window and wall construction. Homes may be built with thick north walls and set 50 percent below the surface of the earth in order to prevent heat loss in winter months from this colder side of a building. Shade trees are planted along the south side to help cool the house in summer.

The advantage of an active system over a passive one is that the heat gained can be stored for use when it is needed—at night or on cloudy days.

Because the science of using energy from the sun is still in its infancy, solar energy alone simply cannot take over and supply all fuel needs of an industrialized nation. But it certainly can help to reduce our use of fossil fuels, which in many areas are now used **exclusively**. Already the sun is being used to provide part of the energy needs of homes and hospitals, schools and airports, offices and other kinds of buildings throughout varied climates. It is clear that this important energy source works; now it is a matter of using it efficiently.

THINKING IT OVER

(1) What are the two kinds of solar energy systems? _____

(2) Describe how a passive system works. _____

_____

STUDYING THE PASSAGE

(1) Find the Main Idea: Choose one answer.
   (a) Solar energy may be an important fuel source in the future.
   (b) The use of the sun as a fuel source is effective, valuable, and needs to become more common.
   (c) Heat from the sun is a nonrenewable resource.
   (d) Using the sun for fuel involves a lot of work. _____

(2) Find the Facts: Mark each of these *true* or *false*.
   (a) Solar energy is scarce. (a) _____
   (b) Fiberglass can be used in wall panels to let sun through. (b) _____
   (c) Not much has been done to develop ways of using the sun's energy. (c) _____
   (d) Active systems use collectors. (d) _____
   (e) Fans can help distribute the heat to other parts of the building. (e) _____
   (f) Solar heat can be stored. (f) _____
   (g) Not much use has been made of the sun for heat. (g) _____
   (h) A knowledge of heat transfer is important in using solar energy. (h) _____

(3) Find the Order: Number the following in the order in which they appear in the passage.
   (a) Solar energy is heating homes and hospitals. (a) _____
   (b) Fossil fuels are being depleted. (b) _____
   (c) Solar energy systems are usually active or passive. (c) _____
   (d) The challenge is to determine ways of making the sun's heat useable. (d) _____
   (e) Bead walls have been used in an Aspen, Colorado air terminal. (e) _____
   (f) Homes may be built with thick walls. (f) _____
   (g) Solar energy cannot replace fossil fuels yet. (g) _____
   (h) Solar energy can be stored in rocks or in water. (h) _____

(4) Go beyond the Facts: Choose one. We can conclude that solar energy:
   (a) Can supply all of our energy needs.
   (b) Is not expensive.
   (c) Will run out in about 1,000 years.
   (d) Is not dependable. _____

(5) Determine the Writer's Style and Technique: Choose one. The writer assumes the reader:
   (a) Knows a lot about solar energy.
   (b) Knows very little about solar energy.
   (c) Cannot follow descriptions of processes.
   (d) Needs diagrams to understand an explanation. _____

(6) Words and Their Meanings: In the passage find the boldface word which fits each of these definitions.

_____ (a) about to happen

_____ (b) not moving

_____ (c) to produce, give off

_____ (d) gives off heat or light

_____ (e) singly, independently

_____ (f) material made up of glass fibers in resin

A DREAM

ABOUT THE PASSAGE   Golda Meir once said: "I pity people who don't have dreams. Great dreams of great things to come. Dreams they believe in." Her dream of an independent, peaceful Jewish state was so strong it shaped her life.

REASON FOR READING   To learn about the life of a powerful, energetic woman.

READ THE PASSAGE

Golda Meir had been fighting a secret battle against cancer of the blood for twelve years when she died on December 18, 1978, at the age of eighty. But such a fight was not unusual, for she had been in the middle of battles all her life. Her most prominent and important battle was the fight for the survival of Israel—the state she helped to build and served as prime minister through five years and one war.

A popular figure, consistently ranked high on lists of the world's most admired people, she was strong-willed, tough, and determined. Her **presence** inspired love and called for respect.

She was a very private person who, despite a certain severity, could be overly sentimental, vulnerable to slights, and emotional. She showed concern for others' problems and was a willing listener to their opinions, even though once she had made up her mind about something she was hard to **dissuade**. She lived a simple life and made much of her humble beginnings, often starting a speech with, "I, the daughter of Moshe Mabovitch who was just an ordinary carpenter . . . ."

Golda Meir was born on May 3, 1898, and grew up in Kiev, Russia. One of her first memories was of her father boarding up the windows and doors of their small house against the rampaging Cossacks, who were threatening death to the Jews. She was only four, but the experience gave her a taste of the struggles before her. Along with the fear, the frustration, and the consciousness of being different came, as she said later, "the profound instinctive belief that if one

wanted to survive, one had to take effective action about it personally."

Her father emigrated to the United States in 1903; there Golda, her mother, and two sisters joined him three years later. They settled in Milwaukee, where her father was a railroad worker.

As a teenager Golda began to have dreams and to show her independent streak. She wanted to become a teacher, but her father told her, "It doesn't pay to be too clever" and refused to let her attend high school. **Undeterred**, she ran away to stay with her sister in Denver, Colorado. She also became interested in Zionism, the movement that believed that Jews should have their own state in their ancient homeland, Palestine.

When she was nineteen, Golda married Morris Meyerson. He was a shy, **introverted**, intellectual sign painter, completely different in personality from Golda, who had become a speechmaker and political activist—she was convinced that her role was to carve out a country for her fellow Jews. In 1921 she persuaded her husband to emigrate to Palestine. They lived for two years on a **kibbutz**. Next they moved to Tel Aviv, and then to Jerusalem, where they had two children, Menahem in 1924 and Sarah in 1926.

Shortly after Sarah's birth Golda and Morris separated. Then in 1928 she had to make the decision, as she states in her autobiography *My Life*, whether to devote herself entirely to her family or to politics and activism, the life for which she yearned. She took her first political job as head of the Women's Labor Council.

Soon she was working with the future leaders

of the Jewish state—David Ben-Gurion, Levi Eshkol, and Moshe Sharett. They recognized her political **acumen** and her powers of oratory and persuasion; over the years they entrusted her with many important jobs. After World War II Ben-Gurion (who, incidentally, convinced her to Hebraicize her name to Meir) dispatched her to the United States to raise funds and attract immigrants. Within weeks she raised fifty million dollars, which was used to buy weapons for his underground army. In 1947 he sent her on another mission—to meet Trans-Jordan's King Abdullah and persuade him not to attack Israel. To keep this trip secret, she went disguised as a peasant.

After Israel declared its independence on May 14, 1948, Ben-Gurion made her ambassador to Russia, then minister of labor, and then foreign minister. In 1965 she retired, but in 1969 when Premier Levi Eshkol suddenly died of a heart attack, she was persuaded to become premier.

As premier she ruthlessly pursued her dream of an independent Jewish nation, responding to any Arab raid or act of terrorism with strong military **retaliation**. It was therefore ironic that she should fall from power by not taking a strong stand against the Arabs before the 1973 October War. Her advisers counseled her against ordering total mobilization of Israel's defense forces and despite her own **qualms**, she agreed.

Israel won the war, but the Egyptians penetrated Sinai, Syrian tanks nearby broke through on the Golan Heights, and more than 2,500 Israelis died.

Meir was heartbroken, but even in retirement she continued to work to realize her dream of a country where the Jewish people might live in peace.

THINKING IT OVER

(1) What was Golda Meir's dream? _____

(2) What was the important decision she made in 1928?_____

_____

(3) Who urged her to change her name? Why? _____

_____

STUDYING THE PASSAGE

(1) Find the Main Idea: Choose one answer.
  (a) How Golda Meir changed her name.
  (b) Golda Meir's political career.
  (c) The story of Golda Meir.
  (d) Why Golda Meir moved to Palestine.   _____

(2) Find the Facts: Mark each of these *true* or *false*.
  (a) Golda Meir died of cancer.   (a) _____
  (b) Golda Meir was known and respected throughout the world.   (b) _____
  (c) After raising three children, she began her political career. (c) _____
  (d) Meir was ashamed of her humble background.   (d) _____
  (e) She was born in Russia.   (e) _____
  (f) She ran away from home because she was unhappy at high school. (f) _____

(g) She emigrated to Palestine in 1921.   (g) _____

(h) She held many important political positions before
becoming premier.   (h) _____

(3) Find the Order: Number the following in the order in which they appear in the passage.

(a) Soon she was working with the future leaders of the Jewish state.   (a) _____

(b) Her father told her, "It doesn't pay to be too clever."   (b) _____

(c) The experience gave her a taste of the struggles before her.   (c) _____

(d) In 1965 she retired.   (d) _____

(e) She had a presence which inspired love and called for respect.   (e) _____

(f) Golda, her mother, and two sisters joined him three years later.   (f) _____

(g) Despite her own qualms, she agreed.   (g) _____

(h) Her two children were born in Jerusalem.   (h) _____

(4) Go beyond the Facts: Which *one* of the following does *not*
describe Golda Meir?

(a) Concerned and warm.

(b) Moody and changeable.

(c) Sentimental and emotional.

(d) Ambitious.

_____

(5) Determine the Writer's Style and Technique: Which *one* of the
following best describes the passage:

(a) Factual.

(b) Emotional.

(c) Sentimental.

(d) Persuasive.

_____

(6) Words and Their Meanings: In the passage find the boldface word which fits
each of these definitions.

_____ (a) with attention turned inward toward oneself

_____ (b) bearing, carriage, or air of a person

_____ (c) uncertainties; fears

_____ (d) to change someone's mind by persuasion

_____ (e) sharpness of mind, acuteness

_____ (f) a collective farm or settlement in Israel

_____ (g) not discouraged; not prevented from acting

_____ (h) repaying in kind; striking back for revenge

Selection 19 — Subject: Philosophy, Logic, and Language
Theme: The Why and How of It

HOW BIG IS THE UNIVERSE?

ABOUT THE PASSAGE   Just as the beginning of the world mystifies us, so does the size of the universe. It is actually impossible to calculate the size of the universe or to know how many stars it contains.

REASON FOR READING   To sort the factual details into a logical explanation for a difficult concept.

READ THE PASSAGE

Scientists are still puzzling over the size of the universe. Some of them believe that there are definite limits to the universe, and others maintain that the universe is **infinite**—with no beginning and no end. One generally accepted theory is that the universe is becoming larger— **galaxies** are moving outward into space and spreading farther and farther apart; some scientists claim that the universe began about thirteen billion years ago from a dense mass and has been expanding outward ever since. A group of British scientists has suggested that the universe is continually beginning, expanding, and dying, only to begin again as mysterious forces create new matter to replace the spaces left by the expansion of the previous stars and galaxies.

No astronomers would be able to give us a measurement of the entire universe, even if it were considered to be **finite**. This is because, in theory, much of the universe is so far away and moving outward so fast that light and radio signals from its galaxies could never reach our instruments; thus we could never **plot** the locations of these bodies. However, we can measure distance within the **observable** universe, and these distances are so great that we must use very large units to describe them.

One of these units is the light-year. One light-year is the distance light travels in one year. If the speed of light is 186,000 miles per second, can you imagine how many miles light can travel in 365 days! If you figure this out, the result is about 5,870,000,000,000 miles or nearly 6 trillion

miles—a distance which is almost **inconceivable**.

Our own solar system is very small compared to a light-year. For example, Mercury is only some 36,000,000 miles away from the sun; the earth is 93,000,000 miles out; and Pluto is about 3,660,000,000 miles from the sun. Moreover, each of the planets is small in size compared with these large distances. Mercury is only 2,910 miles in diameter, the earth 7,910 miles, and Pluto 8,700 miles. As you can see, much of the universe consists of enormous space.

Stars in the universe are grouped together into formations called galaxies. Our solar system, with its 9 planets, their 32 satellites, and a medium-sized star we call the sun, belongs to a galaxy known as the Milky Way. This galaxy contains approximately 100 billion other stars besides our sun. Proxima Centauri, the nearest of these stars, is about 4.3 light-years away; if you traveled toward Proxima at some 17,000 miles an hour—as fast as some of our space flights—it would take you about 177,000 years to arrive. This is enough to make even a **centenarian** feel like an infant.

Yet there are billions of other galaxies such as ours, each containing billions of stars. The spaces between these galaxies are tremendous. On a clear night, we can see a faint, fuzzy, moon-sized patch which is the galaxy Andromeda. It sends light to our eyes from 10 **quintillion** miles, or more than 2 million light-years, away. We can actually see the size and shape of this galaxy, but it is trillions of times farther away than the moon, billions of times farther away than Pluto, and over a thousand times more distant than the faintest individual star the eye can see.

The most distant galaxies now known are about 3.3 billion light-years away. When we see the light from their stars, we are really seeing something that happened over 3 billion years ago, for that is when the light now reaching us began its journey. Thus astronomers have a kind of "time machine" that allows them to look not only outward into space but back into the past. Who knows—with improved telescopes, they may one day be able to look so far back that they can tell us something about the beginning of the universe itself, that is, if there was one.

THINKING IT OVER

(1) What makes it theoretically impossible to measure the size of the universe? _____

(2) What is meant by a light-year? _____

_____

STUDYING THE PASSAGE

(1) Find the Main Idea: Choose one answer.
   (a) Why we need bigger telescopes.
   (b) The vast size of the universe.
   (c) The problems of measuring distances in space.
   (d) How we measure the universe.   _____

(2) Find the Facts: Mark each of these *true* or *false*.
   (a) The speed of light is 186,000 miles per second.   (a) _____
   (b) Mercury is about 36,000,000 miles away from the sun.   (b) _____
   (c) The earth is 93,000,000 miles away from the sun.   (c) _____
   (d) Our solar system is part of the Milky Way.   (d) _____
   (e) Our galaxy contains approximately a billion stars.   (e) _____
   (f) Andromeda is a faintly visible star.   (f) _____
   (g) We can actually see galaxies which are trillions of times farther away than the moon.   (g) _____
   (h) The most distant point astronomers have learned about is a galaxy 3.3 billion light-years away.   (h) _____

(3) Find the Order: Number the following in the order in which they appear in the passage.
   (a) Our solar system is fairly small compared to a light-year.   (a) _____
   (b) Proxima Centauri is the star nearest to our sun.   (b) _____
   (c) This means astronomers have a kind of "time machine."   (c) _____
   (d) There are billions of galaxies such as ours.   (d) _____
   (e) One generally accepted theory is that the universe is becoming larger.   (e) _____
   (f) This is enough to make even a centenarian feel like an infant.   (f) _____
   (g) We can measure distances within the observable universe.   (g) _____
   (h) Stars are grouped together into galaxies.   (h) _____

(4) Go beyond the Facts: Using the information given in the passage, decide which one of the following could happen with further research and development.
   (a) We will be able to watch life on other planets.
   (b) We will be able to look into the future.
   (c) We will be able to measure the size of the universe.
   (d) We will be able to learn something of the past.   ———

(5) Determine the Writer's Style and Technique: Choose two. The passage enables the reader to:
   (a) Learn specific facts.
   (b) Follow a logical explanation.
   (c) Imagine what it would be like to journey into the past.
   (d) See cause and effect.   ——— ———

(6) Words and Their Meanings: In the passage find the boldface word which fits each of these definitions.

_____   (a) groups of stars bound together by gravitational attraction

_____   (b) unimaginable

_____   (c) a person one hundred years or older

_____   (d) having limits

_____   (e) a thousand quadrillions (or 1 followed by eighteen zeros)

_____   (f) without end or boundaries

_____   (g) to show on a chart or map

_____   (h) capable of being seen or detected and measured by scientific instruments

WAR*

ABOUT THE PASSAGE

It is a curious phenomenon of nature that few animals practice the art of war. Animals of the same species may kill each other, but only two species practice the science of organized destruction employing massed numbers in violent combat. Do you know which they are?

REASON FOR READING

The writer of this passage uses allusions. Notice how these add to the meaning in the passage.

READ THE PASSAGE

One day when I went out to my woodpile, or rather my pile of stumps, I observed two large ants, one red, the other much larger, nearly half an inch long, and black, fiercely contending with one another. Having once got hold they never let go, but struggled and wrestled and rolled on the chips **incessantly**. Looking farther, I was surprised to find that the chips were covered with such combatants, that it was not a duellum, but a bellum, a war between two races of ants, the red always pitted against the black, and frequently two red ones to one black. The **legions** of these Myrmidons covered all the hills and vales of my woodyard, and the ground was already **strewn** with the dead and dying, both red and black. It was the only battle which I have ever witnessed, the only battlefield I ever trod while the battle was raging; **internecine** war; the red republicans on the one hand, and the black imperialists on the other. On every side they were engaged in deadly combat, yet without any noise that I could hear, and human soldiers never fought so resolutely. I watched a couple that were fast locked in each other's embraces, in a little sunny valley amid the chips, now at noonday prepared to fight till the sun went down, or life went out. The smaller red champion had fastened himself like a vice to his adversary's front, and through all the tumblings on that field never for an instant ceased to gnaw at one of his feelers near the root, having already caused the other to go by the board; while the stronger black one dashed him from side to side, and, as I saw on looking nearer, had already **divested** him of several of his members. They fought with more **pertinacity** than bulldogs. Neither manifested the least disposition to retreat. It was evident that their battle cry was "Conquer or die." In the meanwhile there came along a single red ant on the hillside of this valley, evidently full of excitement, who either had despatched his foe, or had not yet taken part in the battle; probably the latter, for he had lost none of his limbs; whose mother had charged him to return with his shield or upon it. Or perchance he was some Achilles, who had nourished his wrath apart, and had now come to avenge or rescue his Patroclus. He saw this unequal combat from afar—for the blacks were nearly twice the size of the red—he drew near with rapid pace till he stood on his guide within half an inch of the combatants; then, watching his opportunity, he sprang upon the black warrior. . . . I should not have wondered by this time to find that they had their respective musical bands stationed on some **eminent** chip, and playing their national airs the while, to excite the slow and cheer the dying combatants. I was myself excited somewhat even as if they had been men. The more you think of it, the less the difference. And certainly there is not the fight

*From *Walden*, by Henry David Thoreau.

recorded in Concord history, at least, if in the history of America, that will bear a moment's comparison with this, whether for the numbers engaged in it, or for the patriotism and heroism displayed. For numbers and for **carnage** it was an Austerlitz or Dresden. . . . I have no doubt that it was a principle they fought for, as much as our ancestors, and not to avoid a three-penny tax on their tea; and the results of this battle will be as important and memorable to those whom it concerns as those of the battle of Bunker Hill, at least.

I never learned which party was victorious, nor the cause of the war; but I felt for the rest of that day as if I had had my feelings excited and **harrowed** by witnessing the struggle, the **ferocity** and carnage, of a human battle before my door.

THINKING IT OVER

(1) What species practice the art of war? _____

_____

(2) What is an allusion? _____

_____

(3) How does an allusion make a passage more meaningful for the reader? _____

_____

_____

STUDYING THE PASSAGE

(1) Find the Main Idea: Choose one answer.
  (a) Ants are very warlike insects.
  (b) Battles of ants are similar to those of humans.
  (c) We should control insects.
  (d) It is interesting to observe nature in minute detail. _____

(2) Find the Facts: Mark each of these *true* or *false*.
  (a) These were giant ants, almost an inch long. (a) _____
  (b) Thoreau found the ants in the area where he cut and stored his wood. (b) _____
  (c) The author called the red ants the republicans. (c) _____
  (d) Thoreau could even hear noise from the battling ants. (d) _____
  (e) The ants quit as soon as they were injured. (e) _____
  (f) Musical ants came to the battle to encourage the soldier ants. (f) _____
  (g) Thoreau never learned the outcome of the ant war. (g) _____
  (h) The ants' combat reminds Thoreau of a human battle which he once witnessed. (h) _____

(3) Find the Order: Number the following in the order in which they appear in the passage.
  (a) Ants battled everywhere among the wood chips; it was a war, not a duel. (a) _____
  (b) A black ant was fighting and dismembering his opponent. (b) _____
  (c) Thoreau went out to his woodpile. (c) _____

(d) For the rest of the day the author felt as if he had
     witnessed a real war.

(d) _____

(e) Thoreau focused his attention on two fighters in a little
     wood-chip valley.

(e) _____

(f) At first he saw two large ants fighting.

(f) _____

(g) Each ant army was ready to be victorious or die.

(g) _____

(h) The fighting ants reminded him of the Trojan War and heroes
     of ancient Greece.

(h) _____

(4) Go beyond the Facts: After reading the passage, we could conclude that:

(a) Insects will someday kill each other off.
(b) Life is worth fighting for.
(c) War, when viewed objectively, is a pointless waste of life.
(d) The author asks, ''Why do humans kill each other?''

_____

(5) Determine the Writer's Style and Technique: The author does all of
the following *except* one.

(a) Provides scientific data.
(b) Hints at a comparison.
(c) Lets you form your own conclusion.
(d) Purposely gives details.

_____

(6) Words and Their Meanings: In the passage find the boldface word which fits
each of these definitions.

_____ (a) spread or scattered

_____ (b) distinguished, renowned; outstanding

_____ (c) large units of soldiers

_____ (d) tormented; twined up, cultivated, brought to the surface

_____ (e) savage wildness

_____ (f) great and bloody slaughter

_____ (g) relating to fighting within a group

_____ (h) stubbornness; sticking tenaciously to something

_____ (i) without stopping

_____ (j) took away from; stripped

69

Selection 21 — Subject: Philosophy, Logic, and Language
Theme: Words, Words, Words

WHERE DO THEY COME FROM?

ABOUT THE PASSAGE Words are living things. They come into existence in surprising ways; they change, grow, and sometimes fade from use.

REASON FOR READING To learn how a few words and phrases acquired their meanings.

READ THE PASSAGE

Words and phrases acquire meanings in different ways. Often it is from daily use or through some connection with an experience. Sometimes words are borrowed from other languages. Knowing the origin or **derivation** of words can provide interesting anecdotes or give details about customs in the past. *Helicopter* is a word that comes from two old Greek words: *helix, heliko*—which means "spiral," and *pteron* which means "wing." A helicopter then is "spiraling wings." This meaning is pretty direct. It is true of what we see when we watch a helicopter. The meaning and derivation of the word *bulldozer*, however, is more involved. It gets its meaning from the way people acted and the words they used to describe these actions.

Originally *bulldose* meant to beat severely or to give a sound thrashing. The idea is that such a beating would be a dose suitable for a bull. It also might be **administered** by a bullwhip. Then the verb *bulldoze* came to mean **intimidating** a person by threatening violence. Later *bulldozer* referred to a large pistol or revolver. In the 1920s, when large earth-moving tractors were first manufactured, they were given this name. The idea of changing people's minds by threats was applied to the changing of the **contours** of the earth by pressure.

A phrase that takes its meaning from daily experience is *It's a cinch*, meaning "It's a certainty" or "That's very easy." This expression has been used in the United States since around 1890, and comes from the Southwest. It is from the cinch of a saddle, a wide band or girth which secures the saddle onto the animal. Before riding a horse you must tighten the cinch so the saddle will not slide off. By extension, the word *cinch* came to suggest a grasp of something so firm it could not get away.

Another phrase takes its meaning from a scientific definition. Have you ever heard people say they were "on cloud nine"? The expression describes a feeling of **euphoria** and joy and is based on actual **terminology** used by the United States Weather Bureau. Clouds are divided into classes and each class is divided into nine types. Cloud nine is the cumulonimbus cloud one often sees building up in the sky on a hot summer afternoon. It may reach 30,000 to 40,000 feet. So if you are on cloud nine, you are high up indeed.

You may want to search out the origins of other words on your own. An **unabridged** dictionary or a book on slang or catch phrases will provide you with interesting details of why we say the things we do.

THINKING IT OVER

(1) What are some ways words and phrases acquire meaning? _____

_____

70

STUDYING THE PASSAGE

(1) Find the Main Idea: Choose one answer.
  (a) The history of individual words can be interesting in itself.
  (b) It's important to know where a word comes from.
  (c) The meaning of words never changes.
  (d) It's not difficult to find out where a word or phrase comes from.   _____

(2) Find the Facts: Mark each of these *true* or *false*.
  (a) The meanings of words and phrases hardly ever change.   (a) _____
  (b) *Helicopter* comes from two Greek words.   (b) _____
  (c) Meteorologists have numbered all the clouds.   (c) _____
  (d) *It's a cinch* is an Eastern expression.   (d) _____
  (e) The way *helicopter* got its meaning is pretty direct.   (e) _____
  (f) *Bulldozer* is a Spanish word.   (f) _____
  (g) Learning where words and phrases come from can provide some
      interesting stories.   (g) _____
  (h) An unabridged dictionary often gives helpful information on
      word origins.   (h) _____

(3) Find the Order: Number the following in the order in which they appear in the passage.
  (a) The expression *being on cloud nine* describes a feeling of euphoria.   (a) _____
  (b) Clouds are divided into classes.   (b) _____
  (c) Words and phrases acquire meanings in different ways.   (c) _____
  (d) *It's a cinch* is an Eastern expression.   (d) _____
  (e) It may reach 30,000 to 40,000 feet.   (e) _____
  (f) You may want to search out the origins of other words.   (f) _____
  (g) Later *bulldozer* referred to a large pistol or revolver.   (g) _____
  (h) Before riding a horse you must tighten the cinch.   (h) _____

(4) Go beyond the Facts: Choose one. We can conclude that:
  (a) Words we use as children will probably be common when we
      are adults.
  (b) Words get meaning by the way they are used.
  (c) Languages do not affect each other.
  (d) New words are a rare occurrence.   _____

(5) Determine the Writer's Style and Technique: The author develops the
    passage by using:
  (a) Logical reasoning.
  (b) Descriptive details.
  (c) Examples.
  (d) Metaphors.   _____

(6) Words and Their Meanings: In the passage find the boldface word which fits each of these definitions.

_____ (a) the outlines of a figure, body, or mass

_____ (b) frightening, overwhelming

_____ (c) given or applied

_____ (d) great joy, happiness

_____ (e) not shortened; whole or complete

_____ (f) history of a word

_____ (g) vocabulary of terms used in a particular art, science, or trade

RUBBER SHEET GEOMETRY

ABOUT THE PASSAGE

Can you believe that the curving mirrors of a funhouse illustrate a new branch of math called topology? Since its beginning in the early twentieth century, topology has developed quickly and become of use and interest in areas besides mathematics.

REASON FOR READING

To follow an explanation of a recent development in mathematics.

READ THE PASSAGE

Topology is a twentieth-century branch of mathematics that seems to be so full of tricks, puzzles, and impossibilities that it is almost pure magic. Topology studies the way shapes can be stretched, twisted, scrunched up, turned inside out, or otherwise **deformed** from one shape into another. It focuses on those properties of an object that **endure** when the object is **distorted**. Topology, therefore, is not concerned with measurements, distances, angles, curves, or speeds. Not even shape is important. The only important things are position, insides and outsides, and direction; an object is viewed as a collection of points. Distance between points may change through distortion but their positional order remains the same.

When you study topology you need to keep such things as pencils, paper, rubber bands, scissors, string, doughnuts, and sheets of rubber handy. These all help you to understand the visible **realm** of topology. We can see why topology has the nickname of rubber sheet geometry by looking at a few games involving it.

Take a clay ball and try to distort it without breaking or tearing it; you may mash and stretch it any way you like. As long as you create no shape that has a hole piercing all the way through it, topologists would say all of your clay forms are the same. When children pick up balls of clay, roll them into long snakes, and then flatten them into disks, they are performing the same kind of topological **transformation** as the expert mathematician.

Let's look at another example of topology at work. Take a square of rubber sheet and draw a circle on it. Now pull and stretch this rubber sheet any way you like. Notice how the circle changes in size and shape, yet the inside of circle and the outside do not switch places.

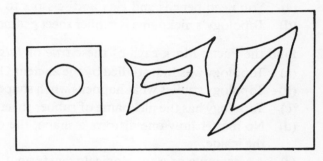

Let us **modify** the above figure by adding five dots to the figure: one dot inside the four dots outside the circle. Now pull and stretch again. Notice that two things will not change: the inner dot cannot be moved outside the circle nor can any of the four outside dots be pushed, pulled, or stretched to cross the line into the circle. Identifying the kinds of properties that endure when a surface is distorted is what interests topologists.

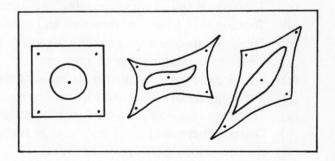

With their fondness for the **abstract**, mathematicians have eagerly developed this science of direction and mathematics of position. Already topology has been put to practical use. It helps in the complicated **programming** of computers, it contributes to the design of geographical maps, it analyzes networks for the distribution of electrical power, water, and natural gas, and it plans traffic control. Not merely an entertaining adventure of the mind, topology has opened new horizons in mathematical thinking.

THINKING IT OVER

(1) According to topology, what are the important characteristics of things?_____

(2) How is topology used? _____

_____

STUDYING THE PASSAGE

(1) Find the Main Idea: Choose one answer.
- (a) Topology studies what remains constant when shapes are deformed.
- (b) Topology is already at work in our modern world.
- (c) You need pencils and clay and scissors to study topology.
- (d) Topology's nickname is rubber sheet geometry. _____

(2) Find the Facts: Mark each of these *true* or *false*.
- (a) Topology was first studied by the ancient Greeks. (a) _____
- (b) Topology studies what happens when shapes are stretched and twisted. (b) _____
- (c) Topology has the nickname of rubber sheet geometry. (c) _____
- (d) No matter how one distorts a shape, the outside always becomes the inside. (d) _____
- (e) An example of a topological transformation is the flattening of a ball of clay into a disk. (e) _____
- (f) No matter how you stretch or pull, the relative positions of the dots remain the same. (f) _____
- (g) Topology focuses on precise measurements, distances, and angles. (g) _____
- (h) At the present time, topology is of interest only to a mathematician. (h) _____

(3) Find the Order: Number the following in the order in which they appear in the passage.
- (a) The inside of the circle and the outside do not switch places. (a) _____
- (b) Topology is full of tricks, puzzles, and impossibilities. (b) _____
- (c) Topology is a science of direction and a mathematics of position. (c) _____
- (d) Topology studies what remains the same when an object is distorted from one shape to another. (d) _____
- (e) Topology has opened new horizons in mathematical thinking. (e) _____
- (f) Topology is not concerned with measurement. (f) _____
- (g) Topology contributes to the design of geographical maps. (g) _____
- (h) Distance between points may change through distortion, but their positional order remains the same. (h) _____

(4) Go beyond the Facts: Choose one. After reading the passage,
we could conclude that:

(a) Positions, insides and outsides, and directions of things can never be expressed in numbers.

(b) Making a ball of clay into a doughnut shape is not a topological transformation.

(c) Topology will be used to create new inventions for our homes.

(d) Topology combines mathematics and art. _____

(5) Determine the Writer's Style and Technique: Which one of the following methods does the writer use to present information?

(a) Using facts to show cause and effect.

(b) Giving examples to show what something is.

(c) Telling a story to illustrate a fact.

(d) Comparing and contrasting to define what something is. _____

(6) Words and Their Meanings: In the passage find the boldface word which fits each of these definitions.

_____ (a) theoretical; not concrete

_____ (b) spoiled the shape of; altered in form as the result of pressure or stress

_____ (c) twisted out of regular shape

_____ (d) sphere, domain; kingdom

_____ (e) to change slightly the form or qualities of something

_____ (f) the act of providing a mechanism, such as a computer, with a program or coded sequence of instructions

_____ (g) the study of those properties of a figure unaffected by a deformation without tearing or joining

_____ (h) conversion; in mathematics, the act of changing the form of something without altering the meaning or value

_____ (i) to last

THE TOPSY-TURVY WORLD OF TOPOLOGY

ABOUT THE PASSAGE   When Leonhard Euler tried to take a Sunday walk 250 years ago, he discovered some principles that would become significant ideas in the twentieth-century development of a new aspect of mathematics called topology.

REASON FOR READING   To follow the reasoning process used to solve a problem.

READ THE PASSAGE

Mathematicians had not really thought about the nature of changing shapes until about 250 years ago when a mathematician named Leonhard Euler became interested in solving a puzzle about bridges.

The Pregel River in the old German city of Konigsberg (now the Russian city of Kaliningrad) was cut by two islands and seven bridges. Someone suggested to Euler that while he was taking his Sunday walk he try to cross all seven bridges without recrossing any of them.

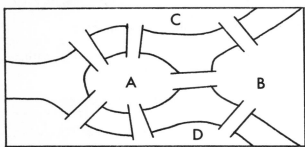

As Euler worked at the problem, he came to realize that the size of bridges was not important, nor was the length or width. Even the distance between them was **irrelevant** to this problem. Everything depended on the positions of the bridges. Euler redrew the map so that the land areas A, B, C, and D were represented by four points. He let the following lines represent the problem:

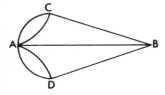

Could he trace all of these lines without retracing any of them? Take a pencil. Can you do it?

The seven bridges could not all be crossed in a continuous walk without retraveling the route at some point. Euler concluded that some **retracing** is **inevitable** whenever there are three or more points at which an odd number of pathways **converge**. You can prove that Euler was right by looking at the following figures. Try to trace all of the lines without retracing any of them. Which two are impossible?

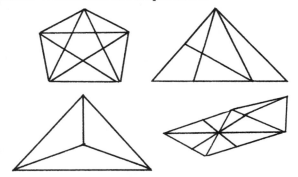

A couple of centuries later Euler's ideas became an important part of a completely new kind of mathematics called topology. While Euler worked on the solution to his problem he realized that the shape of the land masses and the bridges did not matter to his solution. The shapes did not have to be **rigid** and unchanging. He could represent them like this:

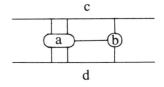

like this,

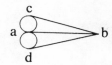

or like this,

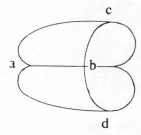

and the problem was the same. The shapes of things didn't matter, but the relationship of the points to each other did. This is an important idea in studying topology.

Changes in the shapes of objects must leave certain basic relationships **unaltered** and the surfaces unbroken. Let's look at a coffee cup and a doughnut. To the topologist, these objects are identical. How can these be topologically the

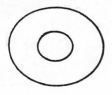 

same? Let's transform the doughnut into a coffee cup to illustrate that they are the same. As you study the series of transformations, notice that the surface is never broken and that we start with just one hole and finish with just one hole. This topological transformation demonstrates

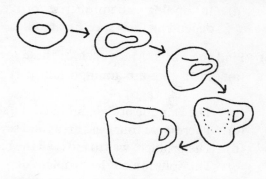

the **property** of the **genus** (defining or identifying nature) of the surface. Roughly speaking, the genus corresponds to the number of holes in the object. Our coffee cup and doughnut belong to genus one because they have one hole. A ball of clay would belong to genus zero, eyeglass frames would belong to genus two, and a pretzel would belong to genus three. Can you see why? To what genus would the following belong: a banana, a phonograph record, and a halloween mask?

THINKING IT OVER

(1)   Why doesn't a topologist see a difference between a coffee cup and a doughnut? _____

_____

(2)   What does genus of the surface mean? _____

_____

(3)   Give answers for the question given in the last line of the passage. _____

_____

_____

STUDYING THE PASSAGE

(1) Find the Main Idea: Choose one answer.
  (a) Retracing is inevitable whenever there are three or more points
      at which an odd number of pathways converge.
  (b) A ball of clay would belong to the genus zero.
  (c) The Konigsberg bridges problem puzzled mathematicians.
  (d) In topology, the properties or basic principles of things do not
      depend on their specific shapes.   _____

(2) Find the Facts: Mark each of these *true* or *false*.
  (a) Ideas that are an important part of topology began over
      200 years ago.   (a) _____
  (b) The Danube bridges initiated the study of topology.   (b) _____
  (c) There were four land areas and seven bridges in the problem. (c) _____
  (d) The problem was to cross all the bridges without retracing any steps. (d) _____
  (e) The solution to the problem depended on the distance
      between the bridges.   (e) _____
  (f) The problem was solved by Albert Einstein.   (f) _____
  (g) Shapes don't have to be rigid and unchanging to be considered
      the same.   (g) _____
  (h) Genus corresponds to the number of holes in an object.   (h) _____

(3) Find the Order: Number the following in the order in which they appear in the passage.
  (a) The Pregel River at Konigsberg was cut by two islands.   (a) _____
  (b) A coffee cup and a doughnut are topologically the same.   (b) _____
  (c) Leonhard Euler became interested in the Konigsberg bridges
      problem.   (c) _____
  (d) Changes in the shapes of objects must leave certain basic
      relationships unaltered.   (d) _____
  (e) The size of the bridges was not important.   (e) _____
  (f) "Genus one" means there is one hole in the surface.   (f) _____
  (g) A couple of centuries later Euler's ideas became an important
      part of topology.   (g) _____
  (h) Some retracing is inevitable whenever there are three or more
      points at which an odd number of pathways converge.   (h) _____

(4) Go beyond the Facts: Which two are true?
  (a) We cannot transform from one genus to another genus.
  (b) A football is an example of genus one.
  (c) Leonhard Euler established the principle of genus.
  (d) In the Konigsberg bridges problem, there were three or more
      points at which an odd number of pathways converged.   _____ _____

(5) Determine the Writer's Style and Technique: Which two are used in this passage.
   (a) Using facts to show cause and effect.
   (b) Giving examples to show what something is.
   (c) Telling a story to illustrate a fact.
   (d) Comparing and contrasting to define something.   _____ _____

(6) Words and Their Meanings: In the passage find the boldface word which fits each of these definitions.

_____ (a) stiff, unbending; inflexible

_____ (b) not related; not applying

_____ (c) to approach the same point from different directions; tend toward a meeting or intersection of paths

_____ (d) category; class of objects with certain common attributes

_____ (e) bound to happen; unavoidable

_____ (f) backtracking; going over again

_____ (g) not changed; the same as before

_____ (h) special characteristic possessed by all members of a category or class; a quality serving to define or describe something

A TWISTED WORLD OF ONE-SIDED FIGURES

ABOUT THE PASSAGE
August Ferdinand Möbius, **theoretical** mathematician and astronomer of the early nineteenth century, was a pioneer in the field of topology. In a **memoir** presented to the French Academy and discovered only after his death, he discussed the properties of one-sided surfaces, including the now celebrated Möbius strip.

REASON FOR READING
To follow instructions that help you visualize a math concept at the same time you are understanding it in written form. You will need scissors, tape, and some medium-weight paper, such as notebook paper, in strips about twelve inches long.

READ THE PASSAGE

Topology is filled with puzzles that are fun to do. Topologists enjoy creating odd shapes and strange objects. Among the most unusual is the **Möbius strip.**

The Möbius strip is hard to imagine but easy to construct. Take a strip of paper about one inch wide and a foot long. Could you draw a **continuous** line on both sides of the paper without lifting the pencil or crossing an edge? Of course not. Now, form the strip into a loop or ring; give one of the ends a half-twist, and tape the ring together so that the "back side" of one end is joined to the "front side" of the other, as shown. This is a Möbius strip.

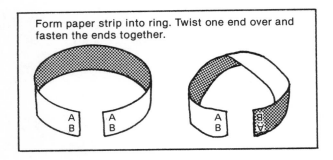

Form paper strip into ring. Twist one end over and fasten the ends together.

Is there an inside and an outside to the ring? Is there a top and a bottom, a front and a back? Here is the way to find out: start a pencil line in the center at any point along the strip and keep drawing down the middle of the strip without ever lifting your pencil. The ends of the line meet, proving that the Möbius strip has only one surface. Break the ring open and lay the strip of paper flat again. Turn it over. Both sides have the pencil line.

Some interesting things happen when you cut a Möbius strip. Make another Möbius strip. Cut down the center line. Do you expect to get one

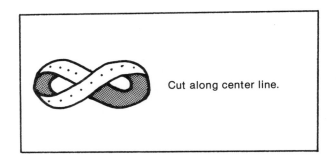

Cut along center line.

or two rings? Draw a line around the new ring you have formed; the line will appear only on one side of the strip! The mathematician's explanation: a Möbius strip has but one edge; the cut adds a second edge and a second side. On the same strip, using the center line you just drew, cut again. Now how many rings do you have? Did you expect this? Why?

Take a new piece of paper and make another Möbius strip. This time begin cutting one third of the way from the edge. Keep cutting, staying the same distance from the edge. What happens is certainly a surprise. The scissors makes two complete trips around the Möbius strip before the cutting line meets itself. The result is two **intertwined** loops. Look carefully at the loops—one is a two-sided hoop, the other is a Möbius strip.

Some practical **applications** of the Möbius strip have been found by inventors. One is a **conveyor belt** shaped like a Möbius strip so that it wears evenly on "both" sides and lasts twice as long! The principle has also been used in electronic resisters, and to make continuous-playing tape recordings that can contain a longer message than an ordinary loop of tape.

Measure 1/3 of the width and begin cutting parallel to the edge.

THINKING IT OVER

(1) What is a Möbius strip? _____

_____

(2) How can you make a Möbius strip? _____

_____

(3) What happens when you draw a pencil line down the middle of a Möbius strip? _____

_____

STUDYING THE PASSAGE

(1) Find the Main Idea: Choose one answer.
   (a) Some unusual characteristics of the Möbius strip.
   (b) Practical uses for mathematical curiosity.
   (c) The Möbius strip has only one surface.
   (d) One can use the Möbius strip to solve math problems. _____

(2) Find the Facts: Mark each of these *true* or *false*.
   (a) Topology is filled with puzzles.   (a) _____
   (b) The odd shapes of topology were created to learn more about the science of motion.   (b) _____
   (c) The Möbius strip has only one surface.   (c) _____
   (d) One can use the Möbius strip to solve math problems.   (d) _____
   (e) The Möbius strip is easy to make.   (e) _____
   (f) Möbius strips have been put to work in programming computers.   (f) _____
   (g) The Möbius strip has only one surface and one edge.   (g) _____
   (h) When you cut along the center line the result is two loops.   (h) _____

(3) Find the Order: Number the following in the order in which they appear in the passage.

    (a) The ends of the pencil line meet.   (a) _____

    (b) Cut along the center line on the twisted paper.   (b) _____

    (c) Take a strip of paper one inch wide and a foot long.   (c) _____

    (d) Draw a line around the new ring you have formed; the line will appear on only one side.   (d) _____

    (e) Give one of the ends a half twist.   (e) _____

    (f) The scissors make two complete trips around the strip.   (f) _____

    (g) Tape the ends of the twisted paper together.   (g) _____

    (h) The result is two intertwined loops.   (h) _____

(4) Go beyond the Facts: Which one is the best conclusion drawn from the passage?

    (a) One can understand topology better by studying the Möbius strip.

    (b) The Möbius strip illustrates some interesting facts to the topologist.

    (c) Topology is just for fun; no one takes it seriously.

    (d) The fact that the pencil line meets itself does not really prove that a Möbius strip has only one surface.   _____

(5) Determine the Writer's Style and Technique: Choose one. In this passage the writer:

    (a) Uses facts to show cause and effect.

    (b) Gives examples to show what something is.

    (c) Tells a story to illustrate a fact.

    (d) Uses comparison and contrast to define something.   _____

(6) Words and Their Meanings: In the passage find the boldface word which fits each of these definitions.

_____ (a) uses to which ideas can be put

_____ (b) without end, without interruption

_____ (c) a continuously moving belt which carries objects from one point to another

_____ (d) having to do with an idea or theory; existing as idea only

_____ (e) an account or report of something worth noticing

_____ (f) twisted together, interlaced

_____ (g) a one-sided surface which can be made from a strip of paper given a half-twist

Selection 25 — Subject: Literature
Theme: Myth, Folklore, and Fantasy

THE END OF THE WORLD

ABOUT THE PASSAGE   In this tale about the end of the world, the author describes a second flood. This one, however, comes in a different way.

REASON FOR READING   To decide whether you are to take this story seriously.

READ THE PASSAGE

It did not come as it came last time. Then it had come in a thunderstorm, continuing its ceaseless downpour until the whole world had been covered. This time it was different. There was no sound of pattering droplets and no sight of falling crystals—in fact there was no rain. But the water continued to come.

There was no warning. It **oozed** its way up through the soil; hidden springs that had once kept the fields so green and fertile, but now were changing them into blankets of sullen **inhospitality**. It **seeped** through every crack of seemingly **barren** rock: tiny, fingerlike trickles which became giant arms as they joined to **engulf** whole mountains. It flowed over river banks that had once been firm and restricting but now were soft and unresisting. It crept out of the sea, **slithering** as a turtle does when she comes ashore to lay her eggs.

The world had never known such a death. It was not like disease or fire or bombs, which could at least be seen and recognized as the enemy. It was far more terrifying. It came as the very life it was destroying, silently and invisibly.

Slowly, **relentlessly**, it brought all humanity to its doom. The black, the yellow, the red and the white; none could escape. And with them went all their inventions, discoveries, and knowledge—the creative efforts of endless generations, lost to the simple elements of hydrogen and oxygen, H_2O. And with all this went the animals, insects, trees, plants, and other living things.

So it continued until the earth was drowned in a valley of swirling liquid which darkened as its depth increased. All the earth was swallowed except for one last mountain peak. Here, two lone **survivors** were on vacation, camping out, blissfully unaware of the calamity that had befallen the planet. One of the campers opened the flap of the tent and walked out. She looked up and saw a great wall of water surging toward her. She turned and quickly went inside, calling to her friend, "For Heaven's sake, Sue, I must have a fever. I had the funniest thing happen to me. I thought I saw a great wall of water surging toward me."

THINKING IT OVER

(1) How does the writer develop her description? _____

_____

(2) Did the end surprise you? How would you have ended it?_____

_____

_____

STUDYING THE PASSAGE

(1) Find the Main Idea: Choose one answer.

    (a) Two against nature.

    (b) How to find water on the top of a mountain.

    (c) How the world drowned.

    (d) On getting wet.   _____

(2) Find the Facts: Mark each of these *true* or *false*.

    (a) There was a heavy rainstorm.   (a) _____

    (b) The green fields became covered with liquid.   (b) _____

    (c) The water came slowly.   (c) _____

    (d) A flood had engulfed the world once before.   (d) _____

    (e) Everything was lost to the elements of nitrogen and oxygen.   (e) _____

    (f) The water continued until the earth was drowned.   (f) _____

    (g) Only two campers were left.   (g) _____

    (h) The camper could not believe her eyes.   (h) _____

(3) Find the Order: Number the following in the order in which they appear in the passage.

    (a) There was one last remaining mountain peak.   (a) _____

    (b) The water seeped through every crack.   (b) _____

    (c) No one would escape.   (c) _____

    (d) There was no sound of rain.   (d) _____

    (e) The earth was drowned.   (e) _____

    (f) It slithered like a turtle.   (f) _____

    (g) Two people were camping.   (g) _____

    (h) It was not like fire.   (h) _____

(4) Go beyond the Facts: The story indicates two of the following:

    (a) Nothing will stop the flood.

    (b) The camper just imagines she sees water at the top of the mountain.

    (c) Humans are powerless in the face of the elements.

    (d) The campers will escape unhurt.   _____   _____

(5) Determine the Writer's Style and Technique: Which method does the writer use?

    (a) Builds up to a climax.

    (b) Ends with an anticlimax.

    (c) Writes in the first person.

    (d) Goes into elaborate detail.   _____

(6) Words and Their Meanings: Find the boldface word which fits each of these definitions. The first definition fits two words.

_____ (a) flowed or leaked out gradually

_____ (b) flowed or leaked out gradually

_____ (c) those who remain alive

_____ (d) unfriendliness

_____ (e) steadily and persistently; pitilessly; unyielding

_____ (f) to swallow; to devour

_____ (g) unproductive; lacking vegetation

_____ (h) slipping and sliding

Selection 26 — Subject: Literature
Theme: Rhythm, Repetition, and Sound

TWO POEMS*

ABOUT THE PASSAGE | Earlier passages discussed white dwarf stars and galaxies from a scientist's point of view; now, here are the viewpoints of two poets. John Updike wrote the first poem after he had read an item in the newspaper announcing the discovery of the smallest star. The author of the second poem is a scientist by profession.

REASON FOR READING | To notice how a poem can present a subject differently from ordinary prose, and to think about what is different about the moods of the two poems.

READ THE PASSAGE

White Dwarf

"Discovery of the smallest known star in the universe was announced today. . . . The star is about one half the diameter of the moon."
                                   —The Times

Welcome, welcome, little star!
I'm delighted that you are
Up in Heaven's vast extent
No bigger than a continent.

Relatively **miniscule**,
Spinning like a penny spool,
Glinting like a polished spoon,
A kind of **kindled demi-moon**,

You offer cheer to tiny Man
'Mid galaxies **Gargantuan**—
A little pill in endless night,
An **antidote** to **cosmic** fright.
                                   —John Updike

Galactic Webs

The stars shall forever trace out
Their endless, but beautiful orbits
Etched in the deep purple skies
Which pervade the vastness
of Limitless space —
And the moon shall circle about
the earth
And the earth, in turn will
entwine the sun
As it weaves its timeless path
Midst the invisible webs woven
by long-forgotten galaxies.
                                   —Samuel T. Fife

*"White Dwarf" © 1962 by John Updike. Reprinted from *Telephone Poles and Other Poems*, by John Updike by permission of Alfred A. Knopf, Inc. The poem first appeared in *The New Yorker* magazine.
"Galactic Webs" printed by permission of Samuel T. Fife.

THINKING IT OVER

(1) Which poem has John Updike imitated? _____

_____

(2) What is the main idea of the Updike poem? _____

_____

(3) What is the main idea of the Fife poem? _____

_____

STUDYING THE PASSAGE

(1) Find the Main Idea: Choose one answer.
   (a) Both poems are about a star.
   (b) Both poems mention the moon.
   (c) Both poems create a feeling of size.
   (d) Both poems compare the size of stars and the earth.   _____

(2) Find the Facts: Mark each of these *true* or *false*.
   (a) The first poet rejoices in the discovery of the smallest star.   (a) _____
   (b) The first poet says the star is smaller than a continent.   (b) _____
   (c) The first poet compares the star to a tarnished spoon.   (c) _____
   (d) The first poet implies that the star is constantly moving.   (d) _____
   (e) The second poet says the circular patterns of the stars' paths
       are beautiful.   (e) _____
   (f) The second poet describes the sky as a deep black.   (f) _____
   (g) The second poet's phrase "earth will entwine the sun" refers to
       the earth's orbital motion during the course of a year.   (g) _____
   (h) The second poet says galaxies weave invisible webs.   (h) _____

(3) Word and Image: A poet chooses words carefully to build an image for
    the reader. The images in both poems involve size.

   (a) What image does Updike present? _____

   (b) Choose three words or groups of words he uses that help build

       this image. _____

   (c) Fife's poem presents a different image. What is it? _____

   _____

   (d) Select three words he uses to create his image. _____

   _____

(4) Go beyond the Facts: What mood does each poem convey?
  (a) Wonder.
  (b) Solemnity.
  (c) Cheerfulness.
  (d) Hope.

  "White Dwarf" _____
  "Galactic Webs" _____

(5) Determine the Writer's Style and Technique: Choose two.
  The second poem gives the impression of size by:
  (a) Describing the arrangement of bodies in space.
  (b) Making comparisons.
  (c) Introducing metaphors.
  (d) Using adjectives.   _____

(6) Words and Their Meanings: Find the boldface word which fits each of these definitions.

  _____ (a) pertaining to a galaxy

  _____ (b) remedy that counteracts the effects of a poison

  _____ (c) amid, in the middle of

  _____ (d) pertaining to the universe

  _____ (e) enormous, gigantic

  _____ (f) set afire; illuminate

  _____ (g) tiny

  _____ (h) half-moon

  _____ (i) printed clearly and permanently on a surface

  _____ (j) to wrap around, twist around

Selection 27 — Subject: Literature
Theme: How Others Have Said It

WORKING FOR CHANGE*

ABOUT THE PASSAGE

Many people have died for ideas they believed in. Robert Kennedy, assassinated in 1968 while speaking out for ideas he valued, had a favorite quotation: "Some see things as they are and say why. I dream things that never were and say, why not." In a tour of South Africa, a country known for its policy of **apartheid**, he directed these words to the young people.

REASON FOR READING

To determine the actions Robert Kennedy valued, to think about the forces he saw as destructive, and to identify what he recommended as solutions.

READ THE PASSAGE

"There is discrimination in this world and slavery and slaughter and starvation. Governments **repress** their people. Millions are trapped in poverty, while the nation grows rich and wealth is **lavished** on **armaments** everywhere.

"These are differing evils, but they are the common works of man. They reflect the imperfection of human justice, the inadequacy of human compassion, our lack of sensibility towards the suffering of our fellows.

"But we can perhaps remember, even if only for a time, that those who live with us are our brothers, that they share with us the same short moment of life, that they seek, as we do, nothing but the chance to live out their lives in purpose and happiness, winning what satisfaction and **fulfillment** they can. . . .

"The answer is to rely on youth, not a time of life but a state of mind, a temper of the will, a quality of imagination, a **predominance** of courage over timidity, of the appetite for adventure over the love of ease. The cruelties and obstacles of this swiftly changing planet will not yield to the **obsolete dogmas** and outworn slogans; they cannot be moved by those who cling to a present that is already dying, who

prefer the illusion of security to the excitement and danger that come with even the most peaceful progress.

"It is a revolutionary world we live in, and this generation at home and around the world has had thrust upon it a greater burden of responsibility than any generation that has ever lived. Some believe there is nothing one man or one woman can do against the enormous array of the world's ills. Yet many of the world's great movements of thought and action have flowed from the work of a single man.

"A young monk began the Protestant Reformation. A young general extended an empire from Macedonia to the borders of the earth. A young woman reclaimed the territory of France, and it was a young Italian explorer who discovered the New World, and the thirty-two-year-old Thomas Jefferson who proclaimed that all men are created equal.

"These men moved the world, and so can we all. Few will have the greatness to bend history itself, but each of us can work to change a small portion of events, and in the total of all those acts will be written the history of this generation.

"Each time a man stands up for an ideal, or

*Excerpted from the eulogy delivered June 8, 1968 by Senator Edward Kennedy at the funeral of his brother, as printed in the *New York Times*.

acts to improve the lot of others, or strikes out against injustice, he sends forth a tiny ripple of hope.

"And crossing each other from a million different centers of energy and daring, those ripples build a current that can sweep down the mightiest walls of **oppression** and resistance. . . .

"Like it or not, we live in times of danger and uncertainty. But they are also more open to the creative energy of men than any other time in history. All of us will ultimately be judged and as the years pass, we will surely judge ourselves, on the effort we have contributed to building a new world society and the extent to which our ideals and goals have shaped that event."

THINKING IT OVER

(1) What does "youth" mean to Kennedy? _____

_____

(2) Quote the line which shows Kennedy's faith in the power of the individual. _____

_____

(3) Identify the monk, the general, the young French woman, and the Italian explorer referred

to in paragraph 6. _____

_____

_____

STUDYING THE PASSAGE

(1) Find the Main Idea: Choose one answer.
   (a) All people are brothers.
   (b) The older generation has made a mess of the world.
   (c) We must each feel the importance of working together for the
       betterment of humanity.
   (d) A young Italian explorer discovered the New World.   _____

(2) Find the Facts: Mark each of these *true* or *false*.
   (a) There is still discrimination, but slavery no longer exists in
       this world.   (a) _____
   (b) All people want to live happy lives.   (b) _____
   (c) The important thing youth can do is to study history and learn
       from the past.   (c) _____
   (d) Thomas Jefferson was twenty-three when he proclaimed all men are
       created equal.   (d) _____
   (e) Each of us individually will bend history according to our acts. (e) _____
   (f) We will judge ourselves according to how much we contributed
       toward building a better society.   (f) _____
   (g) There is no security in clinging to the present.   (g) _____
   (h) The causes of the world's ills lie in human nature itself.   (h) _____

(3) Find the Order: Number the following in the order in which they appear in the passage.
   (a) Each little act of courage will encourage others to action, too. (a) _____
   (b) Governments spend too much money on the arms race. (b) _____
   (c) Young people are courageous. (c) _____
   (d) These are dangerous and uncertain times. (d) _____
   (e) This generation has a great burden of responsibility. (e) _____
   (f) The present era offers more opportunity for progress than any other time in history. (f) _____
   (g) All humans are brothers. (g) _____
   (h) We will judge ourselves. (h) _____

(4) Go beyond the Facts: Choose one. After reading this passage, we could conclude that:
   (a) Robert Kennedy volunteers to solve the world's problems.
   (b) Young people can have an impact on world affairs.
   (c) The older generation must solve the world's problems for the sake of their children.
   (d) Only America can solve the world's problems.

   _____

(5) Determine the Writer's Style and Technique: Choose one. The words Kennedy spoke will be remembered because they are:
   (a) Beautiful and poetic.
   (b) Patriotic.
   (c) Hopeful and encouraging.
   (d) Quoted from other famous people.

   _____

(6) Words and Their Meanings: Find the boldface word which fits each of these definitions.

   _____ (a) the unjust use of force to hold people back

   _____ (b) the importance or prevalence of one thing in comparison with others

   _____ (c) spent abundantly, squandered

   _____ (d) military weapons and supplies for war

   _____ (e) to hold back, keep down

   _____ (f) satisfaction; realization of some plan or hope

   _____ (g) out of date

   _____ (h) doctrines; principles or beliefs considered by those in authority to be the absolute truth

OCEAN VIEW

ABOUT THE PASSAGE   In this account of an imaginary home in an unusual location, the author carefully chooses descriptive details to point out basic differences between this place and the ordinary house.

REASON FOR READING   To notice how the author uses an imaginary experience to identify specific needs for all human environments.

READ THE PASSAGE

They called it Ocean View but it could have been any suburban home or city apartment for that matter. Though perhaps on second thought, it was a little more luxurious than the average home. There was plush wall-to-wall carpeting, the temperature remained automatically at a pleasant 70°, and soft music drifted through the piped-in stereo. The furniture was comfortable, but practical and **sparse**, much of it consisting of built-in cupboards, desks, cabinets, and bookshelves. Even the several television sets nestled into the walls, as did the bunk-type beds. The latter, however, looked very comfortable, with thick mattresses and attractive blue coverlets which matched the flowing drapes at the **panoramic** windows. The bathroom also had wall-to-wall carpeting and was made light and bright by its several mirrors and cheery yellow color scheme. There were two basins with gleaming gold faucets and quite a unique feature—a fresh-water shower. The kitchen was any cook's dream, with many electrical appliances, plenty of counter space, and the inevitable built-ins.

Yes, it was like many other homes I had visited, and yet it did have some unusual features —the fresh-water shower being only one of them. Of course the name "Ocean View" should have clued me into it right away, as well as the gargantuan outside swimming pool and aquarium which they had made so much of in the advertisement. Yet it had never occurred to me when I first read the ad that this new real estate development would actually be under the sea. I

knew that nations were harvesting the sea for food and that in many experiments people had lived below the surface for long periods of time —but having a permanent home down there was something else.

I had wondered what it would be like submerged in the mighty deep. Would I have **claustrophobia** and suffer from feelings of isolation? What would it be like to look out of those enormous windows: to see schools of silvery fish slither by instead of flights of birds in the sky; to watch neighbors glide homeward in eerie, glistening black outfits with shining oxygen tubes strapped to their backs, instead of walking upright on the sidewalk; and to watch the sunset's lengthening shadows along the reefs signal the entrance of the shrimp, lobsters, cardinal fish, and octopuses which replace the more colorful fish of the day, instead of the nocturnal fireflies and moths of **terrestrial** life?

These were the psychological problems to be overcome. But what about the more practical aspects of marine living? Thanks to the creation of new devices that recirculate the air (cleaning and reoxygenating it for rebreathing), moving "outside" could last for as long as four hours and would be relatively simple. Admittedly, I would still have to wear a waterproof suit and carry an oxygen tank, but that probably would be no worse than bundling up in the heavy garments I had to wear each winter when the heavy snowstorms came. The main problem concerning mobility was not the underwater excursions but the return to the world above. Although the house was only fifty feet down, it would not be possible to surface instantly because of *the bends*. People who stay in the depths for long periods must return gradually so that the nitrogen which has been forced into their tissues under pressure is allowed to escape slowly. For if it does not, it forms fatal or crippling gas bubbles which cause intense pain in muscles and joints.

To overcome this problem, the developers of Ocean Properties had supplied special **decompression** tanks. These tanks were located in key places no more than a hundred yards away from most of the houses. They took the occupants to the surface, where they were deposited into a larger and more comfortable decompression chamber. Here the marine dwellers would have to wait for approximately twenty-one hours before encountering normal atmospheric pressure.

I had been assured, however, by the real estate agent who guided me on my tour, that this would really not pose much of a problem because all the **amenities** I would require would be supplied within our own community. And she was sure that if I decided to buy, I would inevitably apply for a position in one of the many undersea businesses and industries being developed. There would be little need for frequent visits to the world above.

I had asked her how one located one's house when there were no roads, pathways or signposts, and all the houses looked the same. For all the houses I had seen consisted of the same two cylindrical metal tanks connected by a short, stout tube. Each one also had the same string of "**umbilical**" lines—electrical and television cables, air hoses, and water lines—streaming shoreward to the life-support unit. She told me that it was simple, as each occupant carried a direction finder which reacted to a sonic pinger located in each home.

Having been reassured that I would indeed find life **congenial**, practical, and entertaining amid the luminous deep, I eventually took the plunge and moved down. Life was indeed far more tranquil than up above, and I soon struck up a friendship with the "natives." In fact, I became particularly close to a grouper (a kind of rock fish) who showed a special **partiality** to lima beans and canned shrimp. I missed my evening smoke: the low-oxygen atmosphere, reduced from the normal 21 percent to 9 percent to compensate for the habitat's 2½ times sea-level pressure, made combustion impossible. Had I been a gourmet, I might also have been frustrated with the **culinary** catastrophes I sometimes had—such as the angel cake which never rose—due to my misjudging the effects of this pressure. However, I took all this in my stride (or perhaps I should say glide!) and quickly adapted to the other inconveniences, such as the variations in sound and pressure which were caused by waves. It was, in fact, no time at all before I became a true **denizen** of the sea.

THINKING IT OVER

(1) How does the writer introduce an element of surprise into this description? _____

_____

(2) What do you think would be the main disadvantages of living under the sea? _____

_____

_____

STUDYING THE PASSAGE

(1) Find the Main Idea: Choose one answer.

    (a) Sea exploration.

    (b) The problems of living under the sea.

    (c) What a typical home under the sea would be like.

    (d) Human attempts to control the sea.   _____

(2) Find the Facts: Mark each of these *true* or *false*.

    (a) The bathroom and kitchen were small and cramped.   (a) _____

    (b) Shrimp, lobster, cardinal fish, and octopus are nocturnal fish.   (b) _____

    (c) New breathing devices enable a swimmer to remain underwater for four hours.   (c) _____

    (d) Bends are prevented by giving the swimmer extra nitrogen.   (d) _____

    (e) The marine dwellers had to remain in the decompression chamber approximately twenty-one hours.   (e) _____

    (f) The oxygen content of the atmosphere was only 9 percent.   (f) _____

    (g) The pressure under the sea is nine times greater than on earth.   (g) _____

    (h) Waves affect the pressure inside the underwater home.   (h) _____

(3) Compare and Contrast: Check which of the following would be done in an underwater terrestrial home.

    (a) Dressing for work.   (a) _____

    (b) Baking an angel-food cake.   (b) _____

    (c) Eating supper.   (c) _____

    (d) Talking to friends.   (d) _____

    (e) Taking a shower.   (e) _____

    (f) Going to and from work.   (f) _____

(4) Go beyond the Facts: Choose three. This passage implies:

    (a) The adaptability of humans may enable them to survive in all sorts of environments.

    (b) Houses under the sea could be comfortable.

    (c) Houses under the sea would be extremely costly.

    (d) Houses under the sea could not be completely self-sufficient.   _____   _____   _____

(5) Determine the Writer's Style and Technique: There are many techniques a writer can use to describe something. Which one of the following does this writer use?

    (a) Specific descriptive details and facts.

    (b) Metaphors.

    (c) Imagery.

    (d) Dramatization.   _____

(6) Words and Their Meanings: In the passage find the boldface word which fits each of these definitions.

_____ (a) resident

_____ (b) giving an unobstructed or complete view in every direction

_____ (c) the pleasant things of life; comforts

_____ (d) fear of being enclosed

_____ (e) relating to the kitchen; cooking

_____ (f) pertaining to release from pressure

_____ (g) of or pertaining to the cord connecting the mother's circulatory system to the fetus in her womb, providing it with nourishment and removing wastes

_____ (h) pertaining to the earth

_____ (i) cheerful, friendly, sociable

_____ (j) showing preference for; fond of

_____ (k) few; not thick

THE MOURNERS*

ABOUT THE PASSAGE   The death of one member of this family brings grief to those who remain. By describing each of the family members, the author, Sir Walter Scott, gives the reader many details about how this family lives and works, about who died and how the others felt about this person.

REASON FOR READING   To notice how Scott systematically develops this mourning scene and how he makes us feel the impact of death upon the family.

READ THE PASSAGE

The body was laid in its coffin within the wooden bedstead which the young fisher had occupied while alive. At a little distance stood the father, whose rugged weather-beaten **countenance**, shaded by his **grizzled** hair, had faced many a stormy night and night-like day. He was apparently revolving his loss in his mind with that strong feeling of painful grief, peculiar to harsh and rough characters, which almost breaks forth into hatred against the world, and all that remain in it, after the beloved object is withdrawn. The old man had made the most desperate efforts to save his son, and had only been withheld by main force from renewing them at a moment when, without the possibility of assisting the sufferer, he must himself have **perished**. All this apparently was boiling in his **recollection**. His glance was directed sidelong towards the coffin, as to an object on which he could not steadfastly look, and yet from which he could not withdraw his eyes. His answers to the necessary questions which were occasionally put to him were brief, harsh, and almost fierce. His family had not yet dared to address to him a word, either of sympathy or consolation. His masculine wife, **virago** as she was, and absolute mistress of the family, as she justly boasted herself, on all ordinary occasions, was, by this great loss, terrified into silence and **submission**, and compelled to hide from her husband's observation the burst of her female sorrow. As he had rejected food ever since the disaster had happened, not daring herself to approach him, she had that morning, with affectionate **artifice**, employed the youngest and favorite child to present her husband with some nourishment. His first action was to push it from him with an angry violence that frightened the child; his next, to snatch up the boy and devour him with kisses. "Ye'll be a bra' fallow, an ye be spared, Patie—but ye'll never—never can be—what he was to me!—He was sailed the coble wi' me since he was ten years auld; and there wasna the like o' him drew a net betwixt this and Buchan-ness—They say folks maun submit—I will try."

And he had been silent from that moment until compelled to answer the necessary questions we have already noticed. Such was the disconsolate state of the father.

In another corner of the cottage, her face covered by her apron, which was flung over it, sat the mother, the nature of her grief sufficiently indicated by the wringing of her hands and the convulsive agitation of the bosom which the covering could not conceal. Two of her gossips, officiously whispering into her ear the commonplace topic of resignation under irremediable misfortune, seemed as if they were endeavoring

*From *The Antiquary* by Sir Walter Scott.

to stun the grief which they could not console.

The sorrow of the children was mingled with wonder at the preparations they beheld around them, and at the unusual display of wheaten bread and wine, which the poorest peasant, or fisher, offers to the guests on these mournful occasions; and thus their grief for their brother's death was almost already lost in admiration of the splendor of his funeral.

But the figure of the old grandmother was the most remarkable of the sorrowing group. Seated on her accustomed chair, with her usual air of apathy, and want of interest in what surrounded her, she seemed every now and then mechanically to resume the motion of twirling her spindle— then to look towards her bosom for the distaff, although both had been laid aside. She would then cast her eyes about as if surprised at missing the usual implements of her industry, and appear struck by the black color of the gown in which they had dressed her, and embarrassed by the number of persons by whom she was surrounded—then, finally, she would raise her head with a ghastly look, and fix her eyes upon the bed which contained the coffin of her grandson, as if she had at once, and for the first time, acquired sense to comprehend her inexpressible **calamity**. These alternate feelings of embarrassment, wonder, and grief, seemed to succeed each other more than once upon her **torpid** features. But she spoke not a word, neither had she shed a tear; nor did one of the family understand, either from look or expression, to what extent she comprehended the uncommon bustle around her. Thus she sat among the funeral assembly like a connecting link between the surviving mourners and the dead corpse which they bewailed—a being in whom the light of existence was already obscured by the **encroaching** shadows of death.

THINKING IT OVER

(1) Why do you think the father was most stricken by the boy's death? _____

_____

_____

(2) How do you think the boy died? _____

_____

(3) How does Scott develop the scene and make us feel the impact of the death upon the family?

_____

_____

STUDYING THE PASSAGE

(1) Find the Main Idea: Choose one answer.
   (a) The younger children are excited about the funeral.
   (b) The grandmother will die soon.
   (c) The father tried to save his son's life.
   (d) This death of a loved one affects everyone in the family, but in different ways.

(2) Find the Facts: Mark each of these *true* or *false*.
- (a) The father had been with the boy at his death.   (a) _____
- (b) The father could not take his eyes off the coffin.   (b) _____
- (c) The father was so upset he would not eat.   (c) _____
- (d) The mother tried to hide her tears.   (d) _____
- (e) Tea and cake would be served at the funeral.   (e) _____
- (f) The mother sat spinning beside the fire to hide grief.   (f) _____
- (g) The grandmother was happy to see all her old friends at the funeral.   (g) _____
- (h) The dead son had been the youngest child in the family.   (h) _____

(3) Find the Order: Number the following in the order in which they appear in the passage.
- (a) The wife had sent the youngest child with food for the father.   (a) _____
- (b) Two village women whisper sympathy to the weeping mother.   (b) _____
- (c) The father stands looking fiercely at the coffin.   (c) _____
- (d) The old grandmother does not understand what is going on around her anymore.   (d) _____
- (e) The grandmother is a link between life and death.   (e) _____
- (f) The coffin lies on the dead youth's own bed.   (f) _____
- (g) The funeral guests will be offered food and drink.   (g) _____
- (h) The father had kissed the young boy.   (h) _____

(4) Go beyond the Facts: Choose the one best conclusion.
- (a) Death is a difficult sorrow for those who live on.
- (b) Death brings great rewards after a hard life.
- (c) It is better to cry and show grief than to try to conceal it.
- (d) Young children and the very old have the best understanding of death.

        _____

(5) Determine the Writer's Style and Technique: The author shows the effect of the death by concentrating his description upon:
- (a) The countryside.
- (b) The moment of death.
- (c) The members of the family.
- (d) The poverty of the cottage.

        _____

(6) Words and Their Meanings: In the passage find the boldface word which fits each of these definitions.

_____   (a) sprinkled and streaked with grey

_____   (b) memory

_____   (c) intruding; gradually taking over the rights or possessions of another; infringing

_____   (d) meekness, surrender, resignation

_____   (e) face

_____   (f) a great misfortune

_____   (g) a woman of great stature and strength; an overbearing woman (The word is used in the passage in its archaic sense of "manlike woman.")

_____   (h) died

_____   (i) cunning, skill: clever trick

_____   (j) lacking in energy or vigor

KÄTHE KOLLWITZ

ABOUT THE PASSAGE | Some people think of art as a luxury, as something to enjoy when they have nothing essential or necessary to do. Some people believe that art should be beautiful. The German artist Käthe Kollwitz believed it was something different.

REASON FOR READING | To learn about the work and ideas of this artist.

READ THE PASSAGE

When Käthe (KAY-tuh) Schmidt was a young girl growing up in Germany in the 1870s, her family encouraged her to draw. She seemed to have an **inclination** to do this well. Her family was a religious one. Her father had trained to be a lawyer, but when he realized he would not be able to put his social ideas and beliefs into practice in Germany as it then was, he trained to become a master **mason**. The influence of her father gave Käthe a feeling of responsibility to help others where she saw it was needed.

At eighteen, she went with her brother to Berlin, she to study art and he to continue his economic and political studies at the university. Through careful, **consistent** practice, she became skilled at drawing and painting. Following graduation in 1891, when she was twenty-four, she married Karl Kollwitz, a doctor, and they settled in a neighborhood of working people in Berlin. There they spent almost the rest of their lives. Karl Kollwitz ran a clinic or **dispensary**. People paid a small sum each week and had their medical needs taken care of. In his waiting room and in the hospital, Käthe Kollwitz found many of the subjects for her art work. Though her first child Hans was born in 1892 and her second son Peter in 1896, she raised her children and did her art work, too.

Her work became concerned with line rather than color, and she began printmaking, which included etching, lithographs, and woodcuts. Her first major group of prints told the story of weavers in the 1840s whose work and livelihood from handloom weaving was being destroyed by the invention and widespread use of power looms. Her prints revealed a story of family poverty, death, **conspiracy**, a procession of angry weavers storming the owner's house, being shot by soldiers, and finally death in the weaver's home. Her prints were unusual because they showed the lives of ordinary people whose sufferings and concerns were often ignored. When the prints were shown in Berlin at the Berlin Art Exhibition of 1898, they were praised highly. Many people were impressed, and the prints were nominated for a gold medal. But the Emperor of Germany vetoed it. He was violently opposed to all art that had any social content. He called it "gutter art."

After this major set of prints, Käthe Kollwitz completed two others: one, "The Peasant's War," showed revolts in sixteenth-century Germany, and the other, "Death," was completed near the end of her life. Between these two cycles she formed sculptures and printed with wood-cuts. Her art is exceptional in revealing the feelings and emotions of people. Many of her prints show human suffering and grief. She may have felt such subjects were more true to life than beautiful pictures would be. She herself knew the suffering of parents, for her own son Hans was killed at eighteen in World War I.

When she was asked to do a drawing or print to help or promote an idea she believed in, she would readily **comply**. Some well-known prints of hers included "Bread," showing two children clinging to their mother's skirts, and "Never Again War!" and "Seed Corn Must Not Be Ground," in opposition to drafting boys for World War II.

Hitler came to power in the 1930s. He banned any art that expressed ideas opposed to Nazism. Käthe Kollwitz's work, along with that of many other artists, musicians, and writers, was declared **degenerate** and banned. Galleries could not show or handle her work. She was in her late sixties and friends urged her to move to a safer country, but she did not want to leave her family. She stayed in Germany and continued to work in spite of these great restrictions.

She was a quiet, strong, shy woman whose art uses large, bold forms and a graceful, delicate line to reveal the emotions and feelings of people. Her art is not joyful, but it shows a truth about life. Even though many of her prints and drawings were destroyed when her house in Berlin was bombed during the war, she left behind a large body of work when she died in 1945.

THINKING IT OVER

(1) What was unusual about Käthe Kollwitz's work? _____

_____

(2) What was the main form Käthe Kollwitz used for her art? _____

_____

STUDYING THE PASSAGE

(1) Find the Main Idea: Choose one answer.
   (a) Käthe Kollwitz worked hard.
   (b) Käthe Kollwitz's work was concerned with revealing a truth about life.
   (c) Käthe Kollwitz created "gutter art."
   (d) Käthe Kollwitz wasn't recognized as an artist.   _____

(2) Find the Facts: Mark each of these *true* or *false*.
   (a) Käthe Kollwitz was a Swedish artist.   (a) _____
   (b) Käthe Kollwitz knew many weavers.   (b) _____
   (c) Käthe Kollwitz showed artistic ability when she was young.   (c) _____
   (d) The family felt a social responsibility.   (d) _____
   (e) Germany's rulers liked Käthe Kollwitz's art.   (e) _____
   (f) Her prints use bold forms and delicate lines to show
       people's emotions.   (f) _____
   (g) The name of one of her print cycles was "Death."   (g) _____
   (h) Käthe Kollwitz devoted all her time to her art work.   (h) _____

(3) Find the Order: Number the following in the order in which they appear in the passage.

    (a)   She had two children.   (a) _____

    (b)   She went to Berlin with her brother to study art.   (b) _____

    (c)   Käthe Kollwitz's work was banned by Hitler.   (c) _____

    (d)   Her art is exceptional in revealing the feelings of people.   (d) _____

    (e)   Her own son Hans was eighteen when he was killed in World War I.   (e) _____

    (f)   She made a print "Seed Corn Must Not Be Ground" to express her opposition to drafting boys for World War II.   (f) _____

    (g)   Her father trained to be a lawyer.   (g) _____

    (h)   The emperor vetoed the prize.   (h) _____

(4) Go beyond the Facts: Choose one. We conclude that Kollwitz's prints would:

    (a)   Reveal some of the happy times in life.

    (b)   Remind us of the human suffering people have in their daily lives.

    (c)   Show an exciting, new style.

    (d)   Poke fun at Germany's rulers.   _____

(5) Determine the Writer's Style and Technique: This passage fits best into the category of:

    (a)   Anecdote.

    (b)   Autobiography.

    (c)   Biography.

    (d)   Fiction.   _____

(6) Words and Their Meanings: In the passage find the boldface word which fits each of these definitions.

    _____   (a)   always the same; showing no variation

    _____   (b)   place where medicine and health care is given

    _____   (c)   tendency to act in a certain way, or to choose to do certain things

    _____   (d)   marked by moral deterioration

    _____   (e)   act in accordance with a request

    _____   (f)   one who works or builds with stone or brick

    _____   (g)   agreement to perform together an illegal act

PICASSO

ABOUT THE PASSAGE

Pablo Picasso is one of the greatest artists of the twentieth century. His greatness came in part from the sheer quantity and variety of art he created. But his personal life, too, was characterized by great variety and intensity.

REASON FOR READING

To learn details of this person's unusual and varied life.

READ THE PASSAGE

You may never have heard his name and you may never have seen his work, yet it is fairly certain that he will have touched you in some way. For as well as influencing the artists of the twentieth century, Pablo Picasso had an impact on the whole range of contemporary art design. Whether it's the print shirt or blouse you are wearing, the pottery figure you received for Christmas, or the magazine ad which caught your eye, it's likely to have been influenced in some way by this legendary figure.

And legendary he was. For one thing, few artists have lived as long as he did: he was a substantial 91 years, 6 months, and 17 days when he died. Few artists have had the fame he had during his lifetime: his name was internationally known and his paintings were seen by millions of people. He was in the limelight as far back as the first decade of this century, and what is more remarkable, he retained this position for much of his life.

Picasso was without question a most **prolific** artist; he did thousands of paintings and drawings. Even today, it is not known exactly how many he completed. The "catalogue raisonne" which lists many of his works up to the early 1960s runs to twenty-three volumes! And when he died, it was estimated that there were between 12,000 and 25,000 works which no one had seen, tucked away in one of his villas.

Unlike the majority of artists, who spend their lives in **abject** poverty, Picasso enjoyed the comforts and advantages of a multimillionaire,

for that is exactly what he was. Admittedly, times had been hard in those days of 1907 when he had worked in a rundown studio on the Rue Ravignan in Paris, but soon his paintings were commanding such high prices that he could afford all sorts of luxuries. In 1931 he bought a chateau near Gisors in France. Later, he acquired a **sumptuous** villa at Cannes, an enormous castle on Mont Ste. Victoire (the hill that Cezanne, an earlier artist, had often painted), and a beautiful retreat at Mongins on the French Riviera, where he died.

It has been said that Picasso's wealth could never be calculated, at least not in terms of money. His **currency** was a pen and a piece of paper. He could acquire almost anything he wanted by putting that pen to work. For example, he once "bought" a villa by signing a set of his lithographs.

Although Picasso enjoyed his wealth, it was an innate spirit rather than money that inspired the exuberance which permeated everything he did. He played hard and he worked hard, even to his last day, which was spent eating and relaxing with friends and painting until 3 A.M. He was a wit, **gregarious** and full of fun, often clowning and dressing up in fantastic masks and doing jigs. He could also, however, be irritable and morose. In later years, he mellowed and became rather withdrawn, preferring more to work than to meet people. In fact, during his very last years, he retreated almost completely from the outside world, leaving his last wife, Jacqueline, to cope with his public and even to buy his paints and canvases.

Picasso was one of the most versatile artists. His paintings and drawings show a variety of different styles and techniques, and he worked in many other forms as well. These included graphics and printing, sculpture, ceramics, collages (which he established as a formal device), and even stage and costume design. He was also one of the most **eclectic** artists, drawing inspiration from nature, from modern-day inventions, and from every human experience imaginable. He not only reflected contemporary times, but drew upon the past; like many other artists, he copied the ideas and styles of other art, from Greek and Roman murals to seventeenth-century Dutch etchings, and from unusual African masks and sculptures to the melancholy drawings of El Greco.

Although he spent most of his life in France, Picasso was Spanish. He was born in Malaga in 1881, the son of a provincial art teacher. Picasso showed talent very early, and by the time he was fifteen he had learned all his instructors could teach. In fact, it is said that his father stopped painting then because he knew he could never surpass this child **prodigy**. The first artists who influenced his work were the Postimpressionists, particularly Toulouse-Lautrec. It was not, however, until he was twenty-one that he developed a particular style of his own. It is then he began what is called his "Blue Period," characterized by **emaciated** elongated figures, with no particular identity beyond their horrible suffering. This was followed by a "Rose Period," when this more cheerful color became dominant and his figures took on a happier, more graceful appearance, reminiscent of those in classical vase paintings and figurines.

A short period of studying African art led to his all-important period, "Cubism," the major revolution in twentieth-century painting. It began with a painting completed in 1907 called "Les Demoiselles d'Avignon," which shattered the art world. It depicted five "Ladies of Avignon," but in the most linear and analytical way. Their faces and bodies were distorted and the emphasis was upon shape and space rather than upon realistic details. What Picasso and Georges Braque, who worked with him in the development of Cubism, were attempting during this period was to create a completely new approach to the methods of visual representation. They tried to be as specific as possible about the location, shape, and density of real objects in a real world. They tried to give an image of these objects which was more detailed, more precise, and truer than what can be seen in a single glance. Picasso thus painted not only what we see of an object but also what we "know" of an object. In this way, he contended, he actually gave a truer image of it.

This new style, which was to affect almost every modern artist, was also reflected in Picasso's sculptures, which took on strange, **unorthodox** shapes. Many of these were created from unusual materials. Some were of wire, which he used particularly in the 1920s, and for others he used all sorts of strange **concoctions**. For example, he created a bull's head from a bicycle saddle and handlebars, and made a baboon from a toy car (its face) and a soccer ball (its stomach).

Picasso's style continued to mature and change. From 1920 onward, his works seemed to become more emotional, revealing his reactions to public issues and private relationships. His reaction to the Spanish Civil War, for example, is seen in the terrifying, dislocated features of "Weeping Women," and in perhaps his most famous painting, "Guernica," painted in 1937, which shows the war as a nightmare. Done in **austere** black, grey, and white, it depicts tortured faces and distorted bodies writhing in agony—his protest of the destruction of the Basque town of Guernica by German bombers.

Whether or not people enjoy Picasso's works, they usually agree that he was probably the most inventive of artists and had tremendous impact upon his contemporaries—not only artists but almost all people living in the twentieth century.

THINKING IT OVER

(1) What are two ways in which Picasso's life and work differed from other artists? _____

_____

(2) What was the difference between the styles of his "Blue" and "Rose" periods? _____

_____

STUDYING THE PASSAGE

(1) Find the Main Idea: Choose one answer.
    (a) The effect Picasso has had upon our time.
    (b) How Picasso developed a new art form.
    (c) The kind of person Picasso was.
    (d) How Picasso was different from other artists.   _____

(2) Find the Facts: Mark each of these *true* or *false*.
    (a) Cubism is characterized by emaciated, elongated figures.   (a) _____
    (b) Cubism was an attempt to create a new approach to the method of visual representation.   (b) _____
    (c) Location, shape, and density of objects was important in Cubism.   (c) _____
    (d) The artists contended that Cubism enabled the viewer to see an image of an object that was truer than real life.   (d) _____
    (e) Picasso was the sole creator of Cubism.   (e) _____
    (f) Picasso's Cubism period was a natural outgrowth of his interest in African art.   (f) _____
    (g) Picasso's Cubism period began in the 1950s.   (g) _____
    (h) None of Picasso's Cubist drawings was in color.   (h) _____

(3) Find the Order: Number the following in the order in which they appear in the passage.
    (a) Picasso enjoyed the comforts and advantages of a multimillionaire.   (a) _____
    (b) Few artists have had the fame he has had.   (b) _____
    (c) He was one of the most eclectic artists.   (c) _____
    (d) His paintings became more emotional.   (d) _____
    (e) Picasso was without question a most prolific artist.   (e) _____
    (f) His father was a painter and art teacher.   (f) _____
    (g) His appreciation of African sculpture led to his work with Cubism.   (g) _____
    (h) He played hard and he worked hard.   (h) _____

(4) Go beyond the Facts: Choose two. Which of the following are true?
    (a) Picasso would have been a better artist if he had stayed with one style instead of trying so many.
    (b) Picasso differed from other artists because of the great quantity and variety of art work he completed.
    (c) It would take some people's life savings to buy just one of his works.
    (d) Picasso eventually became tired of being an artist.   _____   _____

(5) Determine the Writer's Style and Technique: Choose one. The writer's focus is on:

(a) Picasso's personality.
(b) Picasso's personality and artistic styles.
(c) A certain period in Picasso's life.
(d) Certain specific works of art created by Picasso.   —————

(6) Words and Their Meanings: Find the boldface word which fits each of these definitions.

_____   (a) sunk to a low condition; miserable, wretched

_____   (b) unadorned; severely simple

_____   (c) highly productive or inventive

_____   (d) selecting from various sources

_____   (e) not following the usual or accepted way

_____   (f) an extraordinary person, particularly when young

_____   (g) extremely thin

_____   (h) of a great size or splendor, suggesting great cost

_____   (i) enjoying the company of people

_____   (j) mixtures

_____   (k) any form of money